Care Management and Assessment: Practitioners' Guide

DEPARTMENT OF HEALTH
SOCIAL SERVICES INSPECTORATE

SCOTTISH OFFICE
SOCIAL WORK SERVICES GROUP

Care Management and Assessment: Practitioners' Guide

Applications for reproduction should be made to HMSO.
First published 1991
Fourth impression 1993

This guidance has been developed by the Social Services Inspectorate working with professional and administrative colleagues within the Department of Health and in consultation with representatives of local authorities, health authorities/boards, and a number of independent researchers (see Annexe D).

This guidance has been produced in collaboration with the Scottish Office Social Work Services Group.

The text was drafted by Bob Welch of the Social Services Inspectorate.

 Edited and designed by Learning Materials Design:
The Schoolroom, Broughton Village
Milton Keynes, MK10 9AA

ISBN 0 11 321463 4

Contents

¶ Introduction

Care management and assessment constitute the core business of arranging care, which underpins all other elements of community care.

This practice guidance is, therefore, relevant to a large number of people in all care agencies, whether in local authorities, in health authorities/boards, or in the independent sector.

Although care management and assessment relate to basic care practice, they carry wide ranging implications for policy, organisation and management.

For this reason, this practice guidance is divided into three documents aimed at different audiences:

- this *Practitioners' Guide*, setting out good practice
- a *Managers' Guide*, dealing with organisational and training issues
- a *Summary of Practice Guidance*, giving a précis of the key messages, primarily for elected members of local authorities and board members of health authorities and independent agencies but also for managers and practitioners less directly affected by the changes.

The *Summary* is incorporated into both the *Practitioners' Guide* and the *Managers' Guide* to provide all readers with a common starting point.

▶ The scope and purpose of this guidance

Policy guidance describes **what** authorities need to do; this practice guidance is designed to help authorities decide **how** best to implement changes locally.

The practice guidance documents should be read in conjunction with Chapter 3 of the policy guidance on the *NHS and Community Care Act 1990* published by the Department of Health in November 1990 in *Community Care in the Next Decade and Beyond*; the Scottish Office Circular SW11/1991 (and HHD/DGM/1991/40) or the equivalent policy guidance issued by the Welsh and Northern Ireland Offices.

The guidance is based on current views of good practice and will be subject to revision in the light of experience. It recognises that there are already examples of good practice on which care agencies will be able to build, 'to encourage the success stories in one area to become the commonplace of achievement everywhere else' (Sir Roy Griffiths). However, as is made clear in the policy guidance, it is accepted that this will take a number of years to achieve.

The guidance is intended to provide a set of principles which all care agencies are able to own, as a common baseline for negotiating local arrangements. It is, therefore, prescriptive about the process of care management but not about the ways of implementing that process. It rehearses a range of options and explores the associated issues, but stresses that change should be:

- evolutionary in nature
- built on existing strengths
- suited to local circumstances
- agreed by all relevant agencies
- supported by training.

The guidance is confined to the care of adults aged over 18 years, but the same principles may be applied to many aspects of child care practice.

The Summary

The *Summary* explains what is meant by care management and assessment, listing the 'core' tasks that are examined more fully in the *Practitioners' Guide*. It underlines the importance of shared understanding of the term 'need' in the introduction of a needs-led approach. The major changes in attitude, organisation and practice that are required are justified by reference to the benefits accruing to users and carers.

The *Summary* focuses on the main issues for care agencies in terms of organisational options and implications, highlighting the fact that care management and assessment will only work if care agencies collaborate and, both jointly and separately, invest in a substantial programme of training.

The *Summary* concludes with a challenge to members, managers, practitioners and administrators to share in a commitment to change, setting out a timetable for the implementation of the new arrangements.

This Guide

This Guide is designed for all those who work directly with users and carers, whether they are:

- employed by local authorities, health authorities/boards or other community care agencies
- independent contractors such as general practitioners.

The Guide is structured around the seven core tasks involved in arranging care for someone in need:

1 publishing information
2 determining the level of assessment
3 assessing need
4 care planning
5 implementing the care plan
6 monitoring
7 reviewing.

'Action checklists' for practitioners are included at the end of each section to encourage readers to apply the material to their own situation.

An example based on the multiple needs of an elderly person is also included, to give a feel for how care management and assessment may work in practice (see Annexe A).

The guidance spells out the principles of good practice that should underpin the ways in which the needs of all users and carers are handled, whether their needs are simple or complex, and whether the assessment is for the support or protection of the individual.

The organisational issues relating to the implementation of these arrangements, and the training implications for staff, are discussed in the separate *Managers' Guide*.

Summary of practice guidance

¶ Care management and assessment: the process

1 Community care policies challenge all those in the caring services to re-think their approach to arranging and providing care.

2 Care management and assessment lie at the heart of this new approach – 'the cornerstones of quality care' in the words of the White Paper *Caring for People*.

3 Care management and assessment constitute one integrated process for identifying and addressing the needs of individuals within available resources, recognising that those needs are unique to the individuals concerned. For this reason, care management and assessment emphasise adapting services to needs rather than fitting people into existing services, and dealing with the needs of individuals as a whole rather than assessing needs separately for different services.

4 As is evidenced by recent research (see SSI (1991) *Assessment Systems and Community Care*), this represents a significant advance on current practice in which service-linked procedures predetermine assessment outcomes, for example assessing *for* domiciliary day, or residential care.

5 If services are to be made more responsive, it is necessary to identify the disparity between assessed needs and currently available services. This is most effectively achieved where the responsibility for assessing need is separated from that of delivering or managing services. This will entail a progressive revision of organisational structures and procedures, but, above all, a change in attitude and approach by managers and practitioners at every level that amounts to creating a new organisational culture.

6 The rationale for this reorganisation is the empowerment of users and carers. Instead of users and carers being subordinate to the wishes of service-providers, the roles will be progressively adjusted. In this way, users and carers will be enabled to exercise the same power as consumers of other services. This redressing of the balance of power is the best guarantee of a continuing improvement in the quality of service.

▶ What is care management?

7 Care management is the process of tailoring services to individual needs. Assessment is an integral part of care management but it is only one of seven core tasks that make up the whole process:

Stage 1 **Publishing information** Making public the needs for which assistance is offered and the arrangements and resources for meeting those needs.

Stage 2 **Determining the level of assessment** Making an initial identification of need and matching the appropriate level of assessment to that need.

Stage 3 **Assessing need** Understanding individual needs, relating them to agency policies and priorities, and agreeing the objectives for any intervention.

Stage 4 **Care planning** Negotiating the most appropriate ways of achieving the objectives identified by the assessment of need and incorporating them into an individual care plan.

Stage 5 **Implementing the care plan** Securing the necessary resources or services.

Stage 6 **Monitoring** Supporting and controlling the delivery of the care plan on a continuing basis.

Stage 7 **Reviewing** Reassessing needs and the service outcomes with a view to revising the care plan at specified intervals.

As the diagram shows, care management is a cyclical process, in which needs are assessed, services are delivered in response, and needs are re-assessed, leading to a changed service response.

The process of care management *

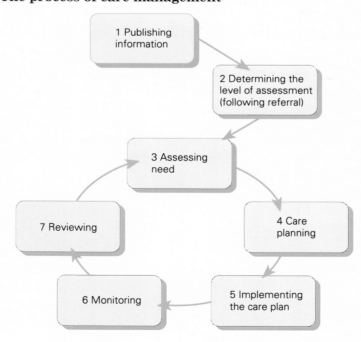

* The term 'care management' is now used in all policy and practice guidance for what was previously termed 'case management'. This change arose from representations made during consultation on draft policy guidance. 'Case' was regarded as demeaning to the individual, and misleading in that is the care, and not the person, that is being managed.

▶ What does care management mean in practice?

8   These core tasks are considered in detail in the *Practitioners' Guide*, but are outlined briefly below. All or most of these tasks may be undertaken by a single practitioner, known as a care manager; or they may be performed by different practitioners. The implications of adopting different organisational arrangements are examined in the *Managers' Guide*.

Stage 1   Prospective users and carers receive information about the needs for which care agencies accept responsibility to offer assistance, and the range of services currently available.

Stage 2   If an enquirer requests more than information or advice, basic information is taken about the needs in question, sufficient to determine the type of assessment required.

Stage 3   A practitioner is allocated to assess the needs of the individual and of any carers, in a way that also recognises their strengths and aspirations. In order to take account of all relevant needs, assessment may bring together contributions from a number of other specialists or agencies. The purpose of the assessment is to define the individual's needs in the context of local policies and priorities and agree on the desired outcome of any involvement.

Stage 4   The next step is to consider the resources available from statutory, voluntary, private or community sources that best meet the individual's requirements. The role of the practitioner is to assist the user in making choices from these resources, and to put together an individual care plan.

Stage 5   The implementation of that plan means securing the necessary finance or other identified resources. It may involve negotiation with a variety of service providers, specifying the type and quality of service required, and ensuring that services are co-ordinated with one another. The responsibility of practitioners at this stage will vary according to the level of their delegated budgetary authority.

Stage 6   Because circumstances change, the implementation of the care plan has to be continuously monitored, making adjustments, as necessary, to the services provided and supporting the users, carers and service providers in achieving the desired outcomes.

Stage 7   At specified intervals, the progress of the care plan has to be formally reviewed with the user, carers and service providers, firstly to ensure that services remain relevant to needs and, secondly, to evaluate services as part of the continuing quest for improvement.

9   At every stage of care management, it is the task of the responsible practitioner to identify and report back any deficiencies in the services available.

▶ What is need?

10   Because care management begins with needs rather than with services, it is essential that all care agencies and practitioners share a common understanding of the term 'need'.

11   Need is a complex concept which has been analysed in a variety of different ways. In this guidance, the term is used as a shorthand for **the requirements of individuals to enable them to achieve, maintain or restore an acceptable level of social independence or quality of life, as defined by the particular care agency or authority**.

12   Need is a dynamic concept, the definition of which will vary over time in accordance with:

- changes in national legislation
- changes in local policy
- the availability of resources
- the patterns of local demand.

13   Need is thus a relative concept. In the context of community care, need has to be defined at the local level. That definition sets limits to the discretion of practitioners in accessing resources.

14   Consequently, there is an onus on elected members and board members to revise the policy framework within which managers and practitioners are asked to operate. A needs-led approach requires needs to be explicitly defined and prioritised in policy statements. Elected members/board members have to ensure on a continuing basis that they are able to resource the response to the needs for which they accept any responsibility.

15   This definition of needs should be incorporated into publicity material which clearly distinguishes between needs that are a mandatory, legislative responsibility and those that are a discretionary duty under the law, assumed as a matter of local policy. The more explicit the definition of need, the clearer users and carers will be about their access to services. By and large, local authorities have wider scope for interpreting their responsibilities in law in relation to the care of adults than to the care of children.

16   In order to have an impact on practice, policy statements must then be translated into operational guidelines that cover all aspects of need. Need is a multi-faceted concept which, for the purpose of this guidance, is sub-divided into six broad categories, each of which should be covered in a comprehensive assessment of need:

- personal/social care
- health care

- accommodation
- finance
- education/employment/leisure
- transport/access.

17   However, need is also a personal concept. No two individuals will perceive or define their needs in exactly the same way. Care management seeks to recognise the individuality of need by challenging practitioners to identify the unique characteristics of each individual's needs and to develop individualised, rather than stereotyped, responses to those needs within the constraints of local policy and resources. Introducing care management should bring major benefits to service users and carers.

▶ What are the benefits of care management?

18   Ten key benefits are listed below and discussed in more detail overleaf.

1 A needs-led approach to assessment and the use of resources, tailoring services to individual requirements.

2 A commitment to individual care planning, specifying desired outcomes.

3 A clear division of responsibility between assessment/care management and service provision, separating the interests of service users and providers.

4 More responsive services as a result of linking assessment and purchasing/commissioning.

5 A wider choice of services across the statutory and independent sectors.

6 A partnership in which users/carers play a more active part alongside practitioners in determining the services they receive.

7 Improved opportunities for representation and advocacy.

8 A way of meeting the needs of disadvantaged individuals more effectively.

9 Greater continuity of care and greater accountability to users and carers.

10 Better integration of services within and between agencies.

1: Tailoring services to needs

19   Care management makes the needs and wishes of users and carers central to the caring process. This needs-led approach aims to tailor services to individual requirements.

20   Where there are separate assessment procedures for different services, this makes for a fragmented approach to people's needs. Furthermore, assumptions can be made about the services people require, and these are what they then receive, without the full range of alternatives having been explored.

21   The aim in future is that assessment procedures will be combined into one integrated process bringing together the contributions from all relevant care agencies, so that the needs of the individual are considered as a whole.

22   It is easy to slip out of thinking 'what does this person need?' into 'what have we got that he/she could have?'. The focus on need is most clearly achieved where practitioners responsible for assessment do not also carry responsibility for the delivery or management of services arising from that assessment.

23   This means that assessment should be established progressively as a separate organisational function that is not tied to any service or set of services. However, this separation has to be done in such a way as to recognise the interdependence of assessment and service provision. Assessment must remain rooted in an appreciation of the realities of service provision, and services must be sensitive to the changing needs of recipients. This calls for a high level of mutual understanding and respect between assessors and service providers.

24   The emphasis on need is further reinforced within the assessment process itself by separating the identification of need from the determination of the service response. The new procedure should thus have two clear stages:

   • assessment of need – the needs of the individual are assessed in the context of the agency's policies and priorities
   • care planning – assessed needs are related to resources.

25   This split should ensure that any gaps between assessed needs and available resources are identified for service planning purposes.

2: Developing commitment to individual care planning

26   The two stages of assessment should come together in the writing of an individual care plan, a copy of which will be given to the user and to other contributors. This will specify:

   • the needs to be met
   • the services to be provided
   • the outcomes to be achieved
   • the means of measuring outcomes.

27   Agreements about services to be provided should be turned into specific objectives for every service provider involved with the user, and set out in an individual care plan. This practice is currently more developed with some user groups than others, for example, individual programme planning for people with learning disabilities.

3: Clarifying responsibilities

28   At present, many practitioners, such as home care organisers, are responsible for assessing and delivering or managing services. They have, therefore, to represent the interests of both user and provider, reconciling within themselves the inevitable tensions between needs and resources.

29   Under the new arrangements, responsibility for defining individual needs and specifying service requirements in terms of the type and quality of care will, over time, be distinguished from responsibility for delivering the services to the specified requirements.

30   This separation does not solve the conflicts between needs and resources, but it does ensure that the respective interests of user and provider are separately represented. This enables any conflicts of interest to be recognised and managed, through a process of negotiation, in a more explicit and accountable manner.

4: Making services more responsive

31   In the past, services have often been purchased centrally, on a block basis, so that practitioners undertaking assessments have had a limited capacity to adapt services to individual needs. Giving purchasing responsibility to practitioners offers them the scope and the incentive to develop new ways of responding to individual needs.

32   Devolved purchasing is one of the most powerful ways of developing more responsive services. Care management projects have shown that this approach can bring about improvements in the choice, cost and quality of the service provided, and also the speed of service delivery.

33   The basic principle is to bring the decision-making as near to the user as possible. However, responsibility does not necessarily have to be devolved to individual care managers. It may be kept at team or district level, particularly in the early stages, while the necessary skills and systems are being developed.

34   Agencies will need to look carefully at the implications of devolved purchasing not only for professional practice but also for management and training.

5: Promoting wider choice

35   Separating assessment from service provision, especially if it is backed by a system of devolved purchasing and improved access to information, gives users and carers a much wider choice of service options.

36   Practitioners undertaking assessments can act as 'brokers' for services from either the statutory or independent sectors, and are in a better position to support informal care networks, because resources are not locked into the budgets for existing services.

6: Enabling partnership with users and carers

37   The fundamental aim of community care is to promote the independence of individuals, so that they are able to live as normal lives as possible. Care management, as the process through which users gain access to services, should reinforce, not undermine, that aim.

38   Because practitioners and their managers control access to resources, the relationship will never be totally equal – but the present imbalance can be corrected by sharing information more openly and by encouraging users and carers, or their representatives, to take a full part in decision-making.

39   The contribution of carers should be formally recognised in new procedures for care management and assessment. Because the interests of users and carers may not coincide, both parties should be given the opportunity of separate consultation with an assessing practitioner. If necessary, carers should be offered a separate assessment of their own needs.

7: Improving opportunities for representation and advocacy

40   The *NHS and Community Care Act 1990* requires local authorities to publish complaints procedures. Users will be able to make representations about either the process or the outcome of an assessment.

41   In addition, the associated policy guidance sets out the expectation that local authorities publish information about:
   • the types of services available across the statutory and independent sectors
   • the criteria for providing services
   • the referral, assessment and review procedures within and between agencies
   • the standards against which care management and assessment will be measured.

42   The introduction of care management will thus create improved opportunities for representation and advocacy:

- users and carers will be better informed about available services

- practitioners, freed of the responsibility for service delivery, can better identify and argue for users' needs

- services can be judged against explicit standards.

43   By separating the interests of service users and service providers, care management establishes a climate in which representation and advocacy can flourish. Local authorities are positively encouraged to promote the development of local advocacy schemes within available resources, giving priority to individuals from previously disadvantaged groups, such as those from black and minority ethnic communities.

8: Meeting the needs of disadvantaged individuals more effectively

44   In the past, mainstream services have not satisfactorily addressed the needs of disabled people and those from black and minority ethnic communities. They have also tended to discriminate against female carers. Care management increases the pressure for change by articulating the specific requirements of individuals from these disadvantaged groups.

45   If agencies are to take full advantage of the opportunities offered by care management to rid themselves of discriminatory practices they will require:

- policies, priorities and objectives framed in consultation with representatives from these disadvantaged groups

- information published in appropriate languages and in accessible forms, for example videos and audio cassettes

- staff recruited and trained from backgrounds of disadvantage similar to those in the communities they serve

- services adapted or newly created to give all users and carers an equal choice

- monitoring systems to measure the achievement of organisational change in this area.

9: Providing greater continuity of care and accountability

46   In their organisational arrangements, care agencies have to balance the requirements of those with short and long-term needs. Care management is a process that is appropriate to both sets of needs but it will have its greatest impact on the care of individuals with long-term needs.

47   Care management stresses the importance of continuity, giving new weight to the monitoring and reviewing of needs so that services can be adjusted to changing circumstances.

48   Although it will not always be possible for the same practitioner
      to retain responsibility throughout, care management
      underlines the importance of one practitioner carrying the co-
      ordinating accountability to the user at each stage of the process.

10: Ensuring better integration within and between agencies

49   Arrangements for care management and assessment will only
      work effectively if they link in with an authority/agency's
      systems for:
      • purchasing and contracting
      • finance and resource management
      • quality assurance and inspection
      • service planning and development
      • staff training and management.

50   Such integration depends on the development of the necessary
      information systems.

51   Inter-agency working at the level of the individual user should
      be facilitated by establishing one co-ordinating practitioner
      across all agencies.

52   Although local authorities have the lead responsibility, this co-
      ordinating function may be delegated to practitioners in other
      agencies, according to the needs of the user.

53   Where such practitioners are given delegated budgetary
      responsibilities and/or access to resources on a cross-agency
      basis, they are better able to cut through the usual difficulties of
      inter-agency co-ordination.

54   In order to ensure that the role of such practitioners is
      acknowledged and respected by all the agencies concerned, it is
      vital that local authorities negotiate the inter-agency care
      management arrangements that are most suited to local
      circumstances.

¶ Care management and assessment: the organisational arrangements

55   It is important to distinguish between care management as a process and the organisational arrangements necessary to implement that process.

56   All users and carers should experience the process of care management, whatever the type or level of their needs. The organisational arrangements will vary both within and between agencies, according to local circumstances. The *Managers' Guide* examines in detail some of the alternative organisational models and their implications.

57   The *NHS and Community Care Act 1990* imposes on local authorities a statutory requirement to co-ordinate arrangements for assessing community care needs on an inter-agency basis by April 1993. In the longer term, these arrangements are expected to fit within more comprehensive systems that realise the benefit of care management for all users and carers. Such systems will take a variety of forms that will emerge from a period of experimentation over the next few years. The expectation at this stage in relation to care management is that local authorities will outline their proposed developments in their community care plans.

58   In seeking to implement principles of care management, all care agencies will face a number of strategic choices:
   • to what types and levels of need and to what standards of care will the agency commit itself (see page 12)
   • to what extent and at what pace will the responsibility for assessment be separated from service provision
   • to what level and at what pace will authority be devolved within the agency, including the authority to purchase services
   • to what extent will the same arrangements apply to adult and child care.

59   The first priority is to establish, in negotiation with other care agencies, the assessment arrangements that have to be in place by April 1993.

▶ Assessment arrangements

60   The specific changes expected of local authorities and health authorities/boards are set out in the third chapter of the policy guidance, *Community Care in the Next Decade and Beyond* and in the *Scottish Office Circular SW11/1991*. These involve ensuring that:
   • information is published about the services available and the means of accessing them, including a complaints procedure

- all relevant care agencies agree how to refer to one another and to co-operate in the assessment of needs that are the responsibility of more than one agency
- the individual care plans resulting from assessment are shared with users, carers and other contributors
- all users in receipt of a continuing service have the benefit of a regular review
- feedback systems exist to identify deficiencies in type, volume or quality of service.

61 However, the major challenge lies in progressively establishing assessment as a separate function within each care agency, distinct from its service-providing arm.

Personnel implications

62 This will involve some degree of re-structuring, and re-deployment and re-training of staff to take account of individuals' total needs, rather than just the specific needs relating to particular services which they may have dealt with in the past. This implies that practitioners will also have a more developed appreciation of when to involve other care agencies in the assessment process.

63 Assessment that seeks to define individual needs, rather than matching services to broad categories of need, calls for a higher level of expertise. This is likely to result in practitioners specialising not only in assessment practice, but in the needs of particular user groups.

64 The inherent danger of assessment becoming divorced from the realities of service provision will have to be countered. Agencies may introduce safeguards such as rotating staff between assessment and service-providing functions, or providing opportunities for practitioners to undertake both functions but in respect of different users. At the very least, agencies will want to maximise the extent to which assessors and service providers are able to influence each other's practice.

65 Agencies will have to establish systems for differentiating levels of assessment in relation to different types of need which make best use of the available personnel, having regard to their number, levels of expertise and experience.

66 Such considerations will also have a bearing on the scope of the assessment role. Particularly where qualified practitioners are in short supply, administrative staff may be given an enhanced role in the sharing of information and the initial identification of need. The tasks in the care management process may be undertaken by a single practitioner or by different practitioners. However, the possible advantages of using a number of practitioners, in terms of staff deployment, must be weighed against the disadvantages of disrupting the continuity of care as experienced by the user.

Co-ordinating procedures

67   The co-ordination of assessment arrangements between agencies is undoubtedly easier where multi-disciplinary teams have been established at either the primary or secondary care level, but locating practitioners together is not of itself a guarantee of improved joint working. Whether housed jointly or separately, practitioners need clearly defined co-ordinating procedures which involve the user in the decision making process.

68   Because assessment is such a crucial part of the arrangements for community care, it will be vital that all agencies set standards by which to monitor their performance.

▶ Care management arrangements

69   Decisions made in the short-term about assessment arrangements will constrain the options available for developing more comprehensive systems of care management at a later date. For this reason, strategic decisions will be necessary at an early stage on:

- the scope and pace of introducing these new arrangements
- the objectives to be achieved
- the priority groups of users
- the level of devolved budgetary responsibility
- the system of accountability.

70   Most authorities and agencies will probably begin by developing care management arrangements for users with complex needs, or those requiring high levels of resources. It is with such user groups – for example, frail elderly people – that projects have demonstrated the effectiveness of care management models. Research has not yet identified the most appropriate way of extending such systems to users with less complex needs. It is, therefore, expected that authorities and agencies will want to experiment with a variety of arrangements before committing themselves to the model(s) most suited to local circumstances.

Different models

71   The eventual goal is to enable **all** users and carers to benefit from some kind of care management arrangement within a proper system of accountability and supervision. Such arrangements may take the form of:

- a single care manager performing all or most of the tasks of care management with varying degrees of budgetary responsibility
- an administrator co-ordinating a range of practitioners
- users acting as their own care managers
- different practitioners assuming responsibility for the various tasks.

72 Care management is most closely associated with the first of these models, because it is the one that most clearly exemplifies the basic principle of arranging care on the basis of an understanding that is developed over time between a practitioner and a user. It has clear advantages over the more indirect co-ordination by an administrator, but it will not be logistically feasible for all users to have their own care manager, and only a small minority of users will be in a position to perform this function for themselves. This means that, for a majority of users, the most likely option will be one in which skilled practitioners are used selectively for such tasks as assessment, with other tasks delegated to support staff.

Devolution of authority

73 The potential of care management arrangements to produce more responsive and innovative services will depend in large measure on the extent to which practitioners are given delegated authority to purchase services. It is the progressive unhitching of resources from existing services that opens up new possibilities for providing care.

74 However, the devolution of the responsibility to allocate resources, changes the nature of the relationship between practitioner and user. Practitioners are less able to act as advocates on users' behalf. This highlights the need to develop opportunities for independent representation and advocacy in parallel with care management arrangements.

Accountability

75 Overall, the advantages to be gained from devolving authority far outweigh the disadvantages – so long as practitioners are sufficiently liberated from organisational constraints to pursue a more entrepreneurial approach. This exposes agencies to an increased risk of both success and failure. They have, therefore, to develop new ways of balancing the increasing autonomy of practitioners with greater accountability for the outcomes of their work.

76 Accountability is even more of an issue in the development of inter-agency care management arrangements because of differences in professional status and organisational structures. In order to make progress, it may be necessary in the short-term to differentiate professional, operational, financial and administrative accountability. In the longer term, it is to be hoped that agencies will evolve joint, or even unified, management arrangements that enable practitioners to access resources on a cross-agency basis. In pursuit of that goal, it is essential that, from the very beginning, care agencies develop their care management arrangements in collaboration with one another (see opposite).

Support systems

77   If care management arrangements are to flourish in any agency, they have to be backed by all the support systems of that agency including:

- service planning
- service contracting
- quality assurance
- management supervision
- training.

78   Such integration is only possible with the benefit of comprehensive information systems. The pace at which such systems are introduced will have a significant influence on the development of care management arrangements.

79   Because these arrangements will be experimental in nature, all agencies should, as a matter of good practice, evaluate their experience and disseminate their findings to other agencies.

▶ Inter-agency arrangements

80   The new care management and assessment arrangements will be most effective when all care agencies in an area work together to provide a 'seamless service' to users. The achievement of that ideal poses a major challenge to all care agencies, underlined by the limited progress to date.

Developing shared values

81   One of the most promising features in recent years has been the emergence of a growing consensus among all care agencies on the values that underpin community care:

- A commitment to ensure that all users and carers enjoy the same **rights of citizenship** as everyone else in the community, offering an equal access to service provision, irrespective of gender, race or disability.
- A respect for the **independence** of individuals and their right to self-determination and to take risks, minimising any restraint upon that freedom of action.
- A regard for the **privacy** of the individual, intruding no more than necessary to achieve the agreed purpose and guaranteeing confidentiality.
- An understanding of the **dignity** and **individuality** of every user and carer.
- A quest, within the available resources, to maximise **individual choice** in the type of services on offer and the way in which those services are delivered.
- A responsibility to provide services in a way that promotes the realisation of an **individual's aspirations and abilities** in all aspects of daily life.

82   The application of such values will not always be straight-forward. For example, it may not be possible to reconcile the independence of the user and the carer; different professions may have differing views on the relative importance of security and risk taking. However, it is only by making values explicit that such differences can be identified and managed.

83   Values, therefore, should be clearly reflected in the policies and practices of every agency. They should also inform the quality standards by which each agency evaluates its own effectiveness.

84   If the core values outlined above are to be owned and shared by practitioners in all care agencies, they will have to be system-atically reinforced by training and supervision at every level. This will provide a solid foundation on which to build collaboration between agencies.

Making agency agreements

85   Consultations between local authorities and other care agencies over community care plans should promote a climate of co-operation and provide the general framework within which to develop collaborative procedures for care management and assessment. Procedures should be negotiated in the context of agency agreements that define respective responsibilities, common objectives and standards of care.

86   Because care management and assessment are central to the development of community care, local authorities and care agencies may designate lead managers to establish and monitor the necessary joint procedures. This may include the setting up of pilot schemes and/or the formulation of common referral and assessment schedules and procedural manuals. Such develop-ments should build on the strengths of existing practices.

87   In the interests of efficiency, inter-agency arrangements should be as simple and straightforward as possible, making selective use of case conferences according to agreed criteria. This will only be possible where there are good networks of both formal and informal communication, founded on mutual trust and understanding.

88   The prospect for co-operation will be enhanced if all care agencies share a common understanding of the care management and assessment process. The *Managers' Guide* examines a number of different options, from partnerships between two agencies to consortia of multiple agencies. What is important in all the models is that the roles, responsibilities and accountability of all practitioners are clearly defined.

89   The greater the authority that is devolved to practitioners, the more flexibility they will have to develop services responsive to individual needs. However, it is recognised that agencies will be dividing responsibilities for the purchasing and providing of services in different ways, over variable timescales. To overcome these difficulties, there will be considerable merit in

agencies pooling their resources and developing joint purchasing arrangements for users for whom there is a shared responsibility, for example, elderly mentally disordered people or people with learning disabilities from long stay hospitals and in the community.

Valuing the contributions of different agencies

90   As local authority social services/work departments have the lead responsibility for community care, social workers and social services staff will carry the major responsibility for performing care management tasks but they will be heavily reliant on the support of other agencies. Some of the key issues for different agencies, discussed in detail in the *Managers' Guide*, are summarised below.

Community nursing and therapy staff

91   Community nurses, by reason of their role and expertise, will also have a crucial role to play. Particularly where health care needs predominate, they may be the most appropriate practitioners to assume the responsibility for care management, or it may be shared with other community health professionals on similar grounds.

92   The aim should be that the practitioner concerned is identified with assessment rather than service provision. Practitioners who retain responsibility for both functions (for example, some therapy staff) may not readily assume care management responsibilities.

93   As collaboration increasingly identifies the overlap between domiciliary and auxiliary nursing care, the coherent delivery of care plans may be enhanced by the development of community care assistants who bridge both roles.

General practitioners

94   General practitioners will have a key role in identifying social care needs and assessing and responding to health care needs. This applies particularly to their surveillance role in respect of people aged over 75 years, but also to two other areas which lie at the interface between health and social services – hospital discharge, and the provision of publicly funded residential and nursing home care. It will be vital that local authorities and health authorities reach agreement on the criteria governing the allocation of resources in these areas.

Hospital-based practitioners

95   The transfer of funding responsibility will place new duties on hospital social workers in terms of accessing the resources necessary to facilitate discharges. By the same token, health professionals will have to come to terms with the fact that, in future, these resources will be cash-limited. All disciplines will have to work together to make best use of the available resources.

Housing

96   While health and social services have traditionally been associated with community care, less recognition has been afforded to the role of housing agencies. Housing has a major bearing on many social and health care needs, so it is essential that housing authorities and housing associations are now made full partners in the assessment process.

Other local authority departments

97   If the needs of the individual are to be considered as a whole, all departments of local authorities must share in the corporate responsibility for community care. This means that service departments such as education, economic development, environmental health, and recreation and leisure, should all be prepared to offer assistance with community care needs.

98   The support of central departments, such as finance and personnel, will also be needed.

Other statutory agencies

99   Local authorities will have to work closely with other statutory agencies, such as police, fire, and criminal justice services, to identify the needs that arise from retaining more dependent and vulnerable people in the community. The way that these agencies collaborate in addressing such needs will be a major factor in establishing public confidence in community care.

Social Security

100   As local authorities assume a greater funding responsibility for community care after April 1993, effective working arrangements with local Social Security offices will take on added significance. Co-operation will help to minimise both delay and duplication in assessing users' financial means.

Independent care agencies

101   Local authorities' funding responsibility will also have an impact on the nature of their relationship with agencies in the private and voluntary sector. Local authorities are expected to adopt an enabling role towards independent care agencies, but increasingly hold them to account on a contractual basis for delivering services to a specified quality and volume. This clarification of responsibilities is intended to safeguard the interests not only of the local authorities and independent agencies, but also of users and carers.

102   Voluntary agencies will not only be expanding the range of service options available to users and carers; they will also be needed to perform an advocacy function in support of users and carers. Where practitioners have delegated authority both to assess need and allocate resources, users' access to independent representation and advocacy is particularly important.

▶ Training

103 The introduction of new arrangements will have to be closely integrated with training that equips managers and practitioners with the necessary knowledge and skills and helps them to learn from their experiences of trying out new ways of working.

104 Because the organisational arrangements will be so diverse, it will be for each agency to determine the level of qualification, training and/or experience that is appropriate to each role. In the short-term, much of the responsibility will fall on in-house training officers. They will need to work closely with education establishments to structure their training modules so that these relate to formal vocational, qualifying and post-qualifying training awards. In this way, practitioners will be able to satisfy their career development needs, while adapting to the requirements of organisational change.

Central role of users

105 It is important that managers and practitioners do not feel de-skilled or daunted by the scale or pace of change, so any training must recognise and build on existing skills. Nevertheless, it will be a fundamental requirement of any training programme that all participants understand and own the values and objectives which underpin the move from a service-led to a needs-led approach.

106 The most effective way of demonstrating the centrality of users' needs and wishes will be by consulting users and carers over the training programme and inviting them to contribute to the training itself. If practitioners are to empower users and carers then they must have a capacity to understand the needs of all users, irrespective of gender, race or disability. Training in anti-discriminatory practice must, therefore, be given a high priority.

Devolution of authority

107 The other major dimension of training will be in helping practitioners to adjust to increased levels of delegated authority, particularly in the management of budgets. In this regard, there may be an overlap in the training needs of managers and practitioners as the new arrangements evolve.

Joint training

108 Because all care agencies have an investment in the new arrangements for care management and assessment, many training needs will be held in common. Collaboration between agencies will be advanced by maximising the opportunities for joint or shared training.

109 Any training strategy will have to be flexible to accommodate changing requirements. Like the care management and assessment arrangements themselves, the training will be refined through a process of experimentation, evaluation and revision.

¶ Commitment to change

110   The re-ordering of organisation and practice, as outlined in this document, will require changes in attitude at every level. Commitment to change has implications for:

- members
- managers
- practitioners
- administrators.

▶ Members

111   The approach of elected members/board members will have a major bearing on the extent and pace of change. They will need to:

- allow users and carers to participate in policy making through consultation procedures
- agree the objectives for change
- revise their statements of policy and priorities to be expressed in terms of needs, rather than services
- match resources to those policies and priorities
- commit their agencies to providing services to specified standards
- enable users and carers to have access to a range of options across the statutory and independent sectors
- endorse the devolution of responsibility and budgetary control, linking finance to needs rather than to services
- accept that mistakes will be made in the interests of promoting more responsive and innovative services.

▶ Managers

112   In implementing the changes managers will need to:

- undertake an appraisal of change options
- take stock of existing resources, strengths and weaknesses
- determine the means of implementing the chosen objectives for change
- secure ownership of the strategy for change through consultation with staff, users, carers and other care agencies
- create space for change management, allowing time for systems development and staff training
- develop new systems of accountability
- devolve responsibility for decision-making and resource allocation
- agree the performance measures used to monitor the changes.

▶ Practitioners

113   Practitioners will be challenged to change their style of working.
      They will need to:

      • acquire needs-led attitudes and approaches

      • develop the skills of needs assessment, defining objectives in
        terms of the outcomes desired by users and carers

      • promote greater participation by users and carers, building
        on their strengths

      • think creatively about service options within and between
        agencies

      • adjust to more devolved responsibility for resource allocation
        and financial management

      • give higher priority to the specification and monitoring of
        quality standards

      • increase their skills in negotiation and co-ordination.

▶ Administrators

114   Administrators will have a key role in developing and managing
      the new systems of working. They will need to:

      • develop procedures that are flexible enough to accommodate
        individual needs

      • revise procedures to reflect the distinction between
        assessment and service provision

      • promote more user friendly information sharing

      • accelerate the development of the necessary information
        systems

      • devise means of monitoring the new systems.

¶ Timetable of implementation

115   Many local authorities and health authorities/boards are aiming to introduce revised arrangements in advance of the formal implementation date. This suggested timetable outlines the basic steps necessary to comply with the minimum requirements.

September 1991

❏ Make strategic choices about:

• separation of assessment and service provision

• devolution of purchasing responsibility.

❏ In England, confirm that the care programme approach for those in contact with specialist psychiatric services and arrangements for hospital discharges have been implemented in accordance with Circulars HC (89) 5 and LAC (89) 7.

❏ Establish implementation groups on revising assessment arrangements and developing care management proposals.

❏ Ensure mechanisms for involving all other care agencies.

❏ Institute review of policy statements to be expressed in terms of needs rather than services.

April 1992

❏ Issue draft proposals on assessment and care management and arrangements for consultation.

❏ Agree criteria for cross-agency referral.

❏ Identify the key personnel in each care agency.

❏ Develop a training strategy.

❏ Set out a strategy for devolving purchasing responsibility.

❏ Confirm the strategy for developing management information systems.

December 1992

❏ Issue revised financial assessment procedures.

❏ Publish criteria for publicly funded placements in residential and nursing homes and the quality standards to be met by such homes.

April 1993

❏ Implement the new assessment arrangements.

❏ Publish community care plan, including proposals for the development of care management arrangements.

September 1993

❏ Initial review of the new arrangements.

❏ Develop pilot care management arrangements.

April 1994

❏ Publish community care plan, with any necessary revision of assessment arrangements.

❏ Initial review of care management pilot arrangements.

Stage 1
Publishing information

To make public the needs for which assistance is offered and the arrangements and resources available for meeting those needs

1.1   As was emphasised in the Summary, care management is about empowering users and carers, enabling them not only to make choices about the services they receive but also to be more in control of the process through which they gain access to services.

1.2   If this objective is to be achieved, an essential feature of the new arrangements will be a greatly increased emphasis on the sharing of information. In this context, information is power. All care agencies will, therefore, need to examine the information they currently publish on:

- the resources/services available
- the assessment and review procedures.

1.3   It is the responsibility of the practitioner to ensure that this published information reaches potential users and carers who are considering seeking assistance. The availability of such material should help practitioners in their task but it will also mean that they will be more open to public challenge on the quality of service they provide. Where practitioners identify deficiencies in the published information available, these should be drawn to the attention of management.

1.4   This published material will set out the needs which should be the focus of practitioners' concern. As outlined in the Summary (page 28–29) it is vital that elected members, managers and pratitioners share a common understanding of those needs.

¶ Process

1.5   Publishing information about the arrangements and resources available for meeting needs will vary according to local policy. However, it should:

- fulfil the requirements of statute and policy guidance
- take account of a number of different audiences
- adopt common principles for the sharing of information.

Stage 1

❶ In England Section 46 and in Scotland Section 52 which inserts a new Section 5A in the *Social Work (Scotland) Act 1968*.

❷ In England Section 50 and in Scotland Section 52 which inserts a new Section 5A in the *Social Work (Scotland) Act 1968*.

❸ In England, para 3.56 of *Community Care in the Next Decade and Beyond* and, in Scotland, para 7 of Scottish Office Circular SW11/1991.

▶ Fulfil the requirements of statute and policy guidance

1.6   Under the terms of the *NHS and Community Care Act 1990* local authorities are required to publish:
  - community care plans ❶
  - complaints procedures ❷.

1.7   This information sets out the general context of service provision and the statutory means of seeking redress if the individual is dissatisfied with the service provided.

1.8   In addition, the associated policy guidance ❸ defines the **information that local authorities are expected to publish in relation to their care management and assessment arrangements.** These are:
  - the types of services available across the statutory and independent sectors
  - the criteria for providing services
  - the referral, assessment and review procedures within and between agencies
  - the standards by which the care management system (including assessment) will be measured.

1.9   This information should be **presented in a readily accessible form** that takes account of potential users who have:
  - a language other than English
  - a different cultural background
  - a sensory impairment
  - a communication difficulty (illiteracy or learning disability).

1.10   Subject to the availability of resources and departmental priorities, **experimentation with media other than the written word,** for example, videos or audio cassettes should be encouraged.

▶ Take account of a number of different audiences

1.11   The publication of this information is of relevance to a number of different audiences.

The public

1.12   It is central to the care management philosophy that potential users and their carers should be advised of their entitlements including the quantity and quality of the services they may receive. Many authorities have already begun to develop such publicity, for example, by publishing charters of rights for users and carers. Considerable importance is attached to the publication of this information because it should:
  - clarify entitlement and allow the public to make an informed choice about whether or not to seek assistance
  - spell out where and how people can seek help
  - define access to a common assessment process.

1.13 Through the published complaints procedure, users and carers are also informed of their entitlement to make representations under the complaints procedure against either the process or the outcome of an assessment. It is recognised, however, that many users and carers will require considerable support to exercise these entitlements, either because of their incapacity or a reluctance born of a sense of dependence and/or powerlessness. As a point of good practice, local authorities should, therefore, promote, within their available resources, **opportunities for independent representation and advocacy.** Details of such services should be included in the published information.

Managers and practitioners

1.14 The published information is also of value to managers and practitioners because it sets out an explicit **framework of expectation.** On the basis of the published information, practitioners should know the standards of performance expected of them by both their employers and the general public. Consequently, practitioners should be consulted on the drafting of the published information.

Elected members

1.15 The publishing of information places a new onus on elected members to enter into public commitments on the type and quality of services they aim to provide and to resource those services accordingly.

1.16 Their particular responsibility is to set the policy framework for this new needs-led approach. This will mean reviewing existing policy statements to ensure that they are **expressed in terms of needs eligible for assistance** rather than types and volumes of services.

1.17 Increased publicity is likely to stimulate more demand so it is vital that **eligible needs are set in priority order.** In this way, managers and practitioners have a clear mandate for determining the allocation of resources. This definition and prioritisation of needs should take full account of the public consultation with users and carers linked to the process of community care planning.

1.18 Where the local authority has defined the needs which it is prepared to meet this will make it more possible to **devolve responsibility to managers and practitioners** for developing innovative ways of meeting them. Elected members will then hold managers to account for satisfying the identified needs rather than for any particular set of services.

Care agencies

1.19 Although the legal requirement to publish information is confined to local authorities, it is expected that other care agencies will follow suit as a matter of good practice. Indeed, for the benefit of the general public, the advantages of pooling information about resources, in the statutory and independent sectors, will be considerable. It will also assist practitioners to have collated directories of information about resources.

▶ Adopt common principles for the sharing of information

1.20 As local authorities, health authorities/boards and other care agencies seek to integrate the way they deliver services, there will be an increasing pressure to develop **shared databases** not only of services but of service users.

1.21 In progressing down this path, it will be vital that **basic principles of confidentiality are observed** and that these are held in common by all agencies.

> **Principles of confidentiality**
>
> - Information should be used only for the purposes for which it was given.
>
> - Information about a user/patient should normally be shared only with the consent of that person.
>
> - Information should be shared on a 'need to know' basis.
>
> - Users and carers should be advised why and with whom information concerning them has been shared.
>
> - All confidential information should be rigorously safeguarded.

Publishing information action checklist

Practitioners can use this list to check the progress their agency is making.

☐ 1 Are policy statements expressed in terms of needs rather than services?

☐ 2 Have needs been set in priority order?

☐ 3 Have users and carers been able to influence the definition of needs?

☐ 4 Is there published information on assessment arrangements?

☐ 5 Does it specify the standards by which the arrangements will be measured?

☐ 6 Does the information give the public a clear understanding of their entitlements to service provision?

☐ 7 Is there published information on access to independent representation and advocacy as well as a complaints procedure?

☐ 8 Is the information presented in an attractive and accessible form?

☐ 9 Does it take account of the communication needs of potential users?

☐ 10 Does the information provide a working framework for practitioners?

☐ 11 Is information being pooled across the statutory and independent sectors?

☐ 12 Do all care agencies adhere to common principles of confidentiality?

Stage 2
Determining the level of assessment

To make an initial identification of need and match the appropriate level of assessment to that need

¶ Process

2.1 The responsibility for allocating the appropriate assessment in response to a presenting need is shared between:

- the reception staff, administrative and/or professional, who collect the initial information
- the senior or managerial staff who allocate the referral for assessment on the basis of this information.

2.2 Between them they have to perform a number of interrelated functions:

- receive enquiries
- give and gather information
- encourage the full participation of the appropriate people
- develop triggers for identifying other significant needs
- designate responsibility for the allocation of the assessment response
- set criteria for decision-making
- identify levels of assessment
- agree priorities for allocation.

▶ Receive enquiries

2.3 Enquiries will be received in a number of ways, from potential users themselves, their carers or other agencies in the form of office visits, telephone calls or letters. By whatever route an enquiry is made, it is essential that the response at the point of contact is:

Welcoming – this has implications for the quality and privacy of reception facilities as well as the manner of reception staff.

Positive – the enquirer should be left with a clear understanding of how the enquiry will be handled.

Proactive – enquiries should be resolved at the earliest possible stage; information and advice may avoid the need for a referral. The point at which an enquiry converts to a referral should be clearly defined and all referrals should receive a prompt acknowledgement.

Informed – reception staff must know the types of services available, how they are accessed and the likely response times for assessment.

2.4   This quality of response may be difficult to achieve in the face of enquirers who are distressed or hostile at having to expose their vulnerability by the very process of asking for assistance. The performance of the most basic reception duties, therefore, requires both training and support. In this way the task of reception staff can be re-defined to relieve more qualified staff.

▶   Give and gather information

2.5   The scope of information gathering at this stage should be limited to that which is essential. Otherwise it runs the risk of alienating the potential user and duplicating the assessment process itself. Whether the initial dialogue is with reception and/or professional staff, it may involve a number of tasks. Particularly if the role of reception staff is to be expanded, the respective responsibilities of administrative and professional staff should be clearly understood.

2.6   **Providing information and advice** – this will involve redirecting inappropriate enquiries. If only advice is required, no more than a minimum of information will be sought and recorded.

2.7   **Providing simple, direct services** – something as simple as the allocation of bus passes can be dealt with quickly and efficiently at a very early stage without complex assessment.

2.8   **Collecting basic information** – if the enquiry becomes a referral, certain basic information must be recorded. If the reason for requiring the information is properly explained, it will be volunteered more readily. Bearing in mind that the majority of referrals are from other care agencies, social services/social work authorities should exercise their lead responsibility in community care by negotiating with these agencies a set of minimum requirements for referral information, whether by phone or in writing, possibly using standardised referral forms.

Stage 2

> **Example of a standardised referral form**
>
> • Name, address, telephone number and age of potential user.
>
> • Name, address, telephone number of enquirer (if different) and their status.
>
> • Name, address and telephone number of GP (NHS number where known).
>
> • The nature of the presenting problem.
>
> • Whether the enquiry is with the consent and knowledge of the potential user (this should be the norm except for the incapacity of the potential user).
>
> • The purpose to be served by any intervention.
>
> • The urgency or risk as perceived by the enquirer.
>
> • The preferred solution (if any volunteered).
>
> • Any special requirements, for example, difference of language or culture, or communication difficulty.
>
> • Any care services that are currently being received.

2.9   **Helping the enquirer to clarify the nature of their request** – some enquirers will have difficulty expressing their needs. Some will be unsure which care agency is responsible for addressing their needs. Yet others will have a fixed idea about the service they require and may need prompting to specify their actual needs. The practitioner will, therefore, have to help clarify the request.

2.10 The aim of this initial information gathering is to establish as quickly and as sensitively as possible, **the urgency, level and complexity of needs** to inform the allocation decision. This will determine the speed and type of assessment response, including whether assessment by any other care agency is required.

▶ Encourage the full participation of the appropriate people

2.11 Many potential users and carers (or third parties) are able and willing to complete standard forms, thus saving staff time; it is only a minority who may require assistance. Involving users/carers from the outset is a means of **setting the tone of partnership** which should characterise the whole process.

Stage 2

❶ Triggers for the cross-referral of elderly persons between social and health care agencies are explored in the report of a multi-agency seminar issued by the School of Social Studies at Nottingham University, entitled *Co-operation and Community Care* (April 1991).

▶ Develop triggers for identifying other significant needs

2.12 In many cases, the presenting request can be taken at face value but all those involved in collecting or analysing this initial information must be **alert to indications of more deep seated or progressive difficulties,** for example, the early stages of degenerative illness or social breakdown. Staff will be helped by the development of checklists or triggers that might uncover other needs warranting more comprehensive assessment or referral to another agency ❶. Such questions could be considered intrusive and should only be asked with the individual's consent.

> **Examples of trigger questions**
>
> - Has there been a bereavement in the last two years?
>
> - Has there been a recent change of accommodation?
>
> - Is this an unsupported individual, living alone?
>
> - Is there evidence of deteriorating health, for example, loss of memory, incontinence or falling?
>
> - Is there a history of mental health problems and/or hospitalisation?
>
> - Is there a history of drug or alcohol abuse?
>
> - Is this individual living on or below the level of income support?
>
> - Is the carer under stress, for example, chronic lack of sleep?

▶ Designate responsibility for the allocation of the assessment response

2.13 The allocation of the appropriate assessment response is a decision which should be undertaken by **designated staff**, usually at senior practitioner or team manager level. It is the responsibility of these staff to make best use of the available personnel, by relating appropriate levels of competence to the assessment of different types and degrees of need. This has particular significance where there are only a limited number of qualified or specialist staff who have to be used selectively for assessing the most complex needs.

▶ Set criteria for decision-making

2.14 Allocation decisions should **consistently apply the same criteria** which should:
   - reflect the policies and priorities set out in the published information on assessment practice
   - judge the urgency of the required response

- take account of the assessment resources available in terms of the number of administrative, vocationally or professionally qualified staff relative to demand
- weigh the options available to meet specific needs which will affect the level and complexity of the assessment required
- use the assessment to make cost-effective use of the available resources.

2.15   As a point of good practice, local authorities should publish their guidelines on timescales for responding to referrals. These guidelines should be monitored and adjusted to keep waiting lists for assessment to a minimum. To avoid unacceptable delays in response where specialist assessment skills are in short supply, it may be necessary for trained ancillary staff to undertake assessments under the supervision of qualified staff. **A designated manager should be held accountable for overseeing any waiting list for assessment.**

2.16   Because allocation decisions sometimes have to be made on the basis of incomplete information, or subsequent experience reveals other needs, **there should be sufficient flexibility for a more comprehensive assessment to be available,** if required. Such instances should be monitored for any lessons that may be learned.

Identify levels of assessment

2.17   Agencies will want to determine their own levels of assessment according to their policies, priorities and available personnel, but as an example, it is possible to distinguish six levels of assessment.

2.18   These levels of assessment are explored further in the *Managers' Guide.*

Stage 2

Levels of assessment

Assessment	Needs	Services	Agency	Staff	Example of service outcome
1 Simple assessment	Simple, defined	Existing universal	Single	Reception or administrative	Bus pass Disabled car badge
2 Limited assessment	Limited, defined, low-risk	Existing, subject to clearly defined criteria	Single	Vocationally qualified	Low-level domiciliary support
3 Multiple assessment	Range of limited, defined, low-risk	Existing in a number of agencies	Multiple	Vocationally qualified or equivalent	Assistance with meals, chiropody and basic nursing
4 Specialist assessment a) simple	Defined, specialist, low-risk	Existing, specialist	Single or multiple	Specialist ancillary	Simple disability equipment
b) complex	Ill-defined, complex, high-risk	Existing and/or new specialist	Single or multiple	Specialist professional	Home adaptation
5 Complex assessment	Ill-defined, inter-related, complex, volatile, high-risk	Existing and/or new individual combinations of service	Single or multiple	Professionally qualified	Speech therapy
6 Comprehensive assessment	Ill-defined, multiple, inter-related, high-risk, severe	Existing and/or new individual combinations of service	Multiple	Professionally qualified and/or specialist professional	Family therapy Substitute care or intensive domiciliary support

Assessment of disabled persons

2.19 The type of assessment response will normally be **related as closely as possible to the presenting need**. However, there is one legally prescribed exception. Where a person appears to be 'disabled' under the terms of the *Disabled Persons (SCR) Act 1986*, the local authority is required to offer a comprehensive assessment, irrespective of the scale of need that is initially presented ❶.

2.20 The manager, responsible for allocation, must, therefore, have a clear understanding of the local authority's interpretation of a 'disabled person' and ensure that staff implement the requirement for a comprehensive assessment consistently.

Allocating a care manager

2.21 Depending upon the model or models of care management adopted by an authority or agency, it may be that only a minority of users with complex needs will be allocated care managers, whereas those with lesser needs will be allocated a practitioner only for the assessment of need with subsequent stages undertaken by different personnel. The basic judgement will hinge on the assessment of the likely duration, change-ability and complexity of need, including an assessment of whether an ongoing relationship between the practitioner and user will be of key importance to the effectiveness of the intervention.

▶ Agree priorities for allocation

2.22 In broad terms, most referrals for assessment will fall into four categories that can be related to the basic objectives of community care. There are those:
   • for whom community living is no longer a possibility or who are at risk, for example, people with intensive personal care needs
   • reliant on others for survival, requiring help with, for example, feeding, toileting
   • reliant on others for support, requiring help with, for example, cleaning, shopping
   • whose functioning or morale is reduced, for example, as a consquence of a depressive illness.

2.23 Most cases requiring statutory or crisis intervention are likely to fall in the first two categories. In **each** of the four categories, people may be rated as having a low, medium or high level of need.

2.24 Any judgement of the appropriate assessment response and level of priority will have to take account of such factors as:
   • the severity or complexity of needs
   • the degree of risk or vulnerability of user or carers

❶ In England Section 47(2) of the *NHS and Community Care Act 1990* and in Scotland, Section 12A of the *Social Work (Scotland) Act 1968* as inserted by Section 55 of the *NHS and Community Care Act 1990*.

Disabled persons are legally defined as:
• in England – *Persons aged 18 or over who are blind, deaf or dumb, or who suffer from mental disorder of any description, and other persons aged 18 or over who are substantially and permanently handicapped by illness, injury or congenital deformity.*❷
• in Scotland – *A chronically, sick or disabled person or a person suffering from mental disorder (being a person in need) to whom Section 12 of the Social Work (Scotland) Act 1968 applies.*

❷ Section 29(1) of the *National Assistance Act 1948*, as amended.

Stage 2

- the level and duration of the projected resources required (whether immediately or in the future)
- the degree of stress experienced by user, carers or other agencies
- the necessity for co-ordination with other care agencies, for example, about hospital discharge or housing transfer
- the length of time already spent on a waiting list, for instance, a higher priority response should be triggered after a specified period on a waiting list.

2.25 The majority of adults who appear to have community care needs are affected by some form of disability but there are some who may be suffering disadvantage (homeless persons, travellers) or other difficulties (drug/alcohol misuse). However, it would be **inappropriate to prioritise purely on the basis of disability** since this would reinforce handicapping social stereotypes. It is not the disability itself which should determine priority but the:

- attitude and aspirations of the individual in relation to his/her disability/disadvantage
- capacity of the individual
- capacity of the individual's carers   } to deal with identified needs
- capacity of other services
- suitability of their living environment.

2.26 It is the interaction of these five elements which determines an individual's level of functioning. Because they are the least tangible of the elements, **attitude and aspiration** are the factors most easily overlooked.

Determining the level of assessment action checklist

Practitioners can use this list to check the progress their agency is making.

☐   1 Has the agency defined the information required to allocate the appropriate level of assessment?

☐   2 Have the responsibilities of reception staff and duty assessment staff been adequately defined?

☐   3 Is the accountability for decision-making in relation to referrals clearly defined?

☐   4 Is the decision-making founded on explicit criteria?

☐   5 Do staff have a clear understanding of the levels of assessment?

☐   6 Has the responsibility for any waiting list for assessment been allocated to a specific manager?

☐   7 Is the assessment response allocated on the basis of need or of service request?

☐   8 Is the system sufficiently flexible to allow for alternative assessment responses as needs emerge?

Stage 2

Stage 3
Assessing need

To understand an individual's needs; to relate them to agency policies and priorities, and to agree the objectives for any intervention

3.1   As has been seen, the assessment of need will require a significant change in attitude and approach by most practitioners. They will have to make conscious efforts to treat the assessment of need as a separate exercise from consideration of the service response. As is indicated by the work commissioned by the Department of Health ❶, few practitioners currently make that distinction, nor are they encouraged to do so by the assessment procedures they are required to operate.

¶   Process

3.2   The assessment of need should broadly follow this sequence:
- negotiate scope of assessment
- choose setting
- clarify expectations
- promote participation
- establish relationship of trust
- assess need
- determine eligibility
- set priorities
- agree objectives
- record the assessment.

▶   Negotiate scope of assessment

3.3   The scope of an assessment should be related to its purpose. Simple needs will require less investigation than more complex ones. In the interests of both efficiency and consumer satisfaction, **the assessment process should be as simple, speedy and informal as possible.** This means that procedures should be based on the principle of what is the **least** that it is necessary to know:
- to understand the needs being presented
- to justify the investment of public resources.

3.4   It follows, therefore, that staff with any responsibility for assessment have to be trained to use their discretion and to target the assessment on the relevant areas of need.

3.5   **The scope of an assessment has to be individually negotiated.** Both the assessing practitioner and the user have to learn what resources the other brings to the assessment process. These will set the limits to the practitioner's investigation, defining which other individuals should be asked to contribute to the assessment, if the individual's needs are to be seen in their proper social context.

3.6   The practitioner has also to decide whether, subject to the consent of the individual, **there are needs which should be referred to other people or other care agencies** for assessment. At any stage of an assessment an assessing practitioner must be able to identify when he/she does not possess the necessary knowledge and skills and to know how to access them.

3.7   The practitioner must also decide, at an early stage, on **the scale of assessment resources,** for example, the amount of staff time and level of expertise, that should be invested in the needs presented by an individual. Broadly speaking, the assessment input should be commensurate with the likely input of care resources or the likely saving on resources by enabling the individual to cope in other ways.

3.8   To help their staff, authorities may wish to develop guidelines on the levels of assessment they consider appropriate for different types of needs. These should include the timescales considered reasonable for their completion. A suggested model of six levels is illustrated on page 42.

3.9   Comprehensive assessments, usually requiring the greatest investments of resources, will be reserved for the minority of users who have complex or severe needs or, once the provision comes into force, are considered disabled ❶ (see page 43). Where there are disabled children approaching adulthood, the assessments of social services/social work, health and education professionals should be brought together to provide the foundation for planning care into adult life.

Inter-related needs

3.10   An example of what may be included in a comprehensive assessment follows the action checklist, on pages 58–59. Such assessments will normally require the participation of a number of agencies. Wherever possible, agencies should conduct their assessments jointly to promote understanding of inter-related needs and minimise any duplication of assessment.Social, emotional, psychological and physical needs all interact with one another, so the total assessment of need is often greater than the sum of the parts. The skill of the assessing practitioner lies in **understanding how needs relate to one another** from the user's perspective. The virtue of a comprehensive assessment is that it enables individuals to be considered as a whole, enhancing the prospect of an integrated response to their needs.

3.11   It will be helpful if the results of all assessments can be co-ordinated before proceeding to the care planning stage but it is recognised that this may not always be possible. The

❶ In England Section 47 (2) of the *NHS and Community Care Act 1990* and in Scotland, Section 12A of the *Social Work (Scotland) Act 1968* as inserted by Section 55 of the *NHS and Community Care Act 1990.*

development of common assessment schedules will assist the
process of collation.

▶ Choose setting

3.12 The assessing practitioner has to decide the **appropriate
location** for an assessment. This may have a material effect on
the outcome. Office interviews may be administratively
convenient but they may also give false results if the interviewee
is not at ease. Interviewees are more likely to relax in their home
setting. However, the advantages of domiciliary assessments
have to be weighed against their cost.

3.13 Where the assessment is concerned with the maintenance of a
person at home, the assessment should take place in that setting.
If users are considering admission to residential or nursing
home care, involving the irreversible loss of their home, they
should always be given the opportunity of experiencing that
setting before making their final decision.

3.14 There may be advantages to some part of the assessment being
undertaken in settings external to the home, for example, day or
residential care settings so that staff have longer contact with
the individual. In such circumstances, assessors will be working
in close collaboration with service providers.

3.15 In considering such options, care should be taken to avoid
exposing individuals to unnecessary disruption. In addition, it is
necessary to avoid assuming that behaviour will be replicated in
other settings. Such considerations may, occasionally, affect
assessment arrangements for hospital discharges.

▶ Clarify expectations

3.16 Practitioners must ensure that users understand:
   • what is involved in the assessment procedures
   • the likely timescale
   • what authority the practitioner holds
   • the possible outcomes
   • their entitlement to information, participation and
     representation.

3.17 Individuals who enter voluntarily into the assessment process
should also be made aware of their entitlement to withdraw at
any stage. Where the assessment is on an involuntary basis, for
example, as a prelude to possible compulsory admission to
psychiatric hospital, it is even more important that the
individuals are helped to understand, as far as they are able, the
nature of the process in which they are engaged. It is less clear
cut where practitioners are dealing with someone, with failing
capacities, for example, relapse of a psychotic illness, where
intervention has been on a voluntary basis but, at a certain
threshold of risk or vulnerability, is likely to tip over into

compulsory action. That threshold should be clearly defined in policy terms and agreed with other relevant agencies, for example, police and health authorities. All practitioners should be clear on the distinction between using assessment as an instrument of social support as opposed to social control. The former offers choices to the user while the latter imposes solutions. The one should not be allowed to shade into the other without all parties appreciating the full implications of that change.

3.18 The expectations of users will have been framed in part by the authority's publicity about its services and by their experience of the initial response. Potential users may define their needs in terms of services of which they have knowledge, so the greater their knowledge, the less constrained will be the definition of their needs. The more publicity clarifies the **range** of options for particular needs, the less assessing practitioners are likely to be confronted by potential users with preconceived ideas about specific service responses.

3.19 To an extent, the general public has been conditioned into the service-led approach of practitioners. If care management developments free resources so that services can be adapted to individual needs, **assessing practitioners will have to educate potential users to the possibilities of such a system**. It is much easier to define needs in terms of existing services than to fashion a unique definition of an individual's particular needs for which new types of service may be required. It will be difficult for public and staff alike to unlearn existing habits, for example, describing referrals concerned with difficulties in coping at home as applications for residential care.

▶ Promote participation

3.20 The practitioner has to judge how the potential user can be actively involved in the assessment process. Some users will have a clear understanding of their needs; others will have a more ill-defined view of them or the cause of their difficulties; yet others will require the support of representatives to express their feelings. Some find it easy to talk; others may prefer to write, for instance, keeping an assessment diary as a way of recording what people, places and activities are important to them. Some may prefer to demonstrate their difficulties in practice.

3.21 To promote participation, it is necessary for the practitioner to identify the strengths as well as the weaknesses of an individual. Potential users must be helped to appreciate what they themselves are able to contribute, not only what they may require. An assessment should help both the practitioner and the potential user to balance the positives and negatives in the latter's situation. In so doing, potential users are helped to feel that they are being regarded as whole persons and the practitioner will be enabled to place their needs in perspective.

3.22 All users and carers should be encouraged to participate to the limit of their capacity because a passive role will only reinforce a sense of dependence. The more users and carers participate, the more they will be committed to act on the outcome of the assessment.

3.23 Users and carers should receive every help to speak and act for themselves by ensuring that:
- staff have, wherever possible, the appropriate communication skills in terms of language, cultural understanding or technical skills, including signing
- users and carers have ready access to communication equipment and to interpreters or communicators, where assessment staff do not possess such skills
- the use of interpreters or communicators in no way disadvantages users or carers from also having an independent representative, if that is their wish.

3.24 Indeed, there should be a clear distinction between those who have the skills to assist users and carers in articulating their wishes and those who are authorised to act on behalf of users who are either unable to express their own views or wish to be independently represented.

Representation and advocacy

3.25 Users and carers should be given every assistance and opportunity to represent their own interests. Where it is clear, however, that a user or carer would benefit from independent advocacy, **they should be given information about any schemes funded by the authority or run locally.** Consideration should also be given to training in self-advocacy skills.

3.26 By separating assessment and care management from service provision, the practitioner is in a better position to act as an advocate for the user in negotiations with service-providers. However, to the extent that such practitioners are given delegated responsibility for allocating resources to users and carers, they may find difficulty in acting as advocates, and will need to be aware of a possible conflict of roles. There may, therefore, be circumstances where independent advocacy is considered the best option.

3.27 Irrespective of such developments, it is consistent with the aims of basing service provision on the needs and wishes of users that those who are unable to express their views, for example, those with severe learning disabilities or dementia or those who have been previously disadvantaged, for example, those from minority ethnic groups should, as a matter of priority, be supported in securing independent representation. This applies particularly to such users who have no acceptable friend or relation to speak on their behalf. Such users are likely to require an advocate/befriender on a long-term basis, whereas others

Stage 3

may only require such assistance on a short-term basis, for example, in devising the original care plan or in the event of disagreement with the practitioner or agency. All such arrangements must recognise that, at times, the interests of users and carers may be in conflict.

3.28 The introduction of care management will encourage the development of more local advocacy schemes, so practitioners will have to develop the necessary skills for working with such representatives. This will mean ensuring that representatives have access to the necessary information, are able to consult appropriate persons to establish the best interests of the individual and have a safe-guarded role in contributing to the decision-making process.

3.29 Issues associated with advocacy schemes are examined further in the *Managers' Guide*, as well as in the practice guidance on complaints procedures.

▶ Establish relationship of trust

3.30 The practitioner has to establish a relationship of trust with potential users and carers; the more personal the needs, the more important is that trust. In order to appreciate needs from the perspective of users themselves, assessors have to rid themselves, as far as possible, of their own prejudices. The tasks of **listening, observing,** and **understanding** place great demands on staff. The practitioner has not only to hear what is being said but to relate to the feeling with which it is being conveyed. Assessment involves considerable skill in inter-personal relations. All assessment staff should be aware of their limitations and know when to involve others with more specialist expertise or cultural understanding.

3.31 Paradoxically, trust will be fostered by a willingness to support users and carers to make representations under the complaints procedure if they are dissatisfied with either the process or outcome of the assessment.

▶ Assess need

3.32 The practitioner has to **define, as precisely as possible, the cause of any difficulty.** The same apparent need may have many different causes. For example, someone with learning disabilities may be under-functioning through lack of knowledge or understanding, loss of confidence or depression, or as a consequence of some breakdown in relationships. **The proper identification of the cause is the basis for selecting the appropriate service response.**

3.33 The assessment should normally be guided by what the potential user volunteers as the presenting problem, only probing further with the individual's consent. There is a fine line to be drawn between simply accepting what users say they need and possibly reinforcing their low expectations of service, and delving for problems that the user does not perceive as significant. Where there are sound practical or therapeutic reasons for such exploration, these should be explained. The possible danger of wide-ranging assessments is that users are made to feel they have needs which they have never hitherto considered, thereby creating further unnecessary dependency and/or wasteful allocation of resources, for example, unused equipment.

3.34 Need is unlikely to be perceived and defined in the same way by users, their carers and any other care agencies involved. The practitioner must, therefore, aim for a degree of consensus but, so long as they are competent, the users' views should carry the most weight. Where it is impossible to reconcile different perceptions, these **differences should be acknowledged and recorded,** as they may contribute to the evolving understanding of an individual's needs over time. Where there is significant disagreement between users and carers, it may be appropriate to offer the carers the opportunity of a separate assessment of their needs.

3.35 Ultimately, however, having weighed the views of all parties, including his/her own observation, the assessing practitioner is responsible for defining the user's needs. That definition should be recorded and openly shared with the user and other contributors to the assessment, subject to the constraints of confidentiality. The recording of that definition should clearly distinguish between **facts** and the practitioner's **interpretation** of those facts.

3.36 One of the most difficult tasks for the practitioner is to disentangle the range of needs and understand how they interact with one another and with the needs of the user's family and friends. This analysis may have to be provisional at the initial assessment stage and to be revised during reviews of the user's needs, after services have been provided.

▶ Determine eligibility

3.37 Once they have assessed the need, practitioners must decide on the **eligibility of users for assistance from their own agency.** This involves relating individual circumstances to the types of need that have been defined in policy statements as warranting intervention. The more explicit the policy statements, the more readily users and carers can hold practitioners to account for their decision-making.

3.38 Such policy statements should target resources in terms of:
- levels of risk, for example, abuse, lack of support
- tasks of self-care, for example, feeding, toileting
- needs of carers, for example, respite
- other elements deemed necessary to a minimum quality of life, for example, social contact.

At the end of this first stage of assessment, users should know:

- who has taken the decision on eligibility, the assessing practitioner or more senior personnel

- which needs are, or are not, eligible for assistance and why

- which needs may be eligible for assistance from other care agencies

- when, and under what circumstance, they may request reassessment

- the means of complaining, if dissatisfied.

3.39   Assessing practitioners must, unless there are grounds for compulsory intervention, respect the entitlement of any potential user to decline the assistance for which they are considered eligible.

▶ Set priorities

3.40   Having established the needs for which assistance is available, the assessing practitioner and user have to come to some agreement on their relative priorities.

3.41   It will be comparatively easy to distinguish between:
- immediate needs, for example, health crisis or breakdown of personal care
- acute short-term needs, for example, home care following fractured hip
- chronic long-term needs, for example, continuing support in personal care.

3.42   However, in ranking priority, the practitioner will first want to identify:
- those needs of most concern to the potential user
- those needs of most concern to any carer
- those needs which the potential user and/or carer is most motivated to address
- those needs on which intervention is acceptable to the potential user and/or carer.

3.43   The assessing practitioner will again be in a position of having to reconcile or to record potential differences between the parties involved. Individuals may set very different priorities on apparently similar needs. The practitioner's understanding of this perceived priority has to be rooted in an appreciation of the user's aspirations.

3.44   The priorities of users will then have to be matched against those of the authority or agency, which should also be spelled out in policy statements; in complex cases the priorities of a number of agencies may have to be taken into account.

3.45 Agencies may wish, for example, to specify that priority will be given to the maintenance or restoration of independence.

3.46 This will translate into giving priority to:

- needs for domiciliary support, for example, home adaptation or domiciliary care
- remediable needs, for example, recovery from stroke
- increasing needs without any intervention, for example, self-neglect
- potential needs requiring preventive intervention, for example, carer stress.

▶ Agree objectives

3.47 The final stage in the assessment of need consists in agreeing the objectives to be met for each of the prioritised needs. In framing these objectives, the assessing practitioner should take full account of the wishes and aspirations of users and carers. It is they, above all, who must own these objectives. Far from being unrealistic or over ambitious in the objectives they set, potential users from deprived or disadvantaged circumstances are often very modest in their expectations.

3.48 As far as care agencies are concerned, objectives will fall into four main categories:

- promoting or restoring the independent functioning of users/carers
- maintaining care for the users
- providing substitute care
- arranging support for carers.

3.49 There is a tendency for these purposes to be confused, different parties having their own interpretation of the objectives to be achieved. However, the effectiveness of any intervention can only be measured if there is agreement about the objective from the outset.

3.50 To have any value, objectives must be capable of being measured. This is comparatively easy when it relates to quantitative goals, like the speed or frequency of completing self-care tasks, but is more difficult for qualitative goals where, for example, social well-being may have to be measured by indicators such as contact time with friends.

3.51 These objectives, in relation to needs, are the benchmarks against which all the subsequent stages of care management have to be measured. **Objective setting is, therefore, the key to effective care management.**

Stage 3

▶ Record the assessment

3.52 All assessments are likely to be recorded on some kind of proforma. However, such documents must be used with discretion. They should act as a help and not a hindrance to the process of understanding. The collection of unnecessary data can only serve to alienate. A standardised format is more suited to quantitative information, for example, practical difficulties of daily living, than to qualitative information, for example, what is really worrying a person. In the course of recording, the individuality of need must not be lost.

3.53 If users and carers are to play a more active part in their own assessment, there is no reason why many of them should not complete all, or most, of their own proformas. The design of proformas should allow for such participation. The challenge lies in drafting proformas that are friendly to both users and computers, combining narrative recording with appropriate codings. Proformas should distinguish between fact and opinion and between data that is essential for service monitoring or planning and that which is discretionary as an aid to understanding individuals' needs. **Existing proformas should be reviewed in order to confirm that they focus the assessment on needs**, without categorising those needs in terms of services, for example, listing domiciliary support as home care. Such **a review will usefully bring together the views of practitioners, users and carers** so that there is a common sense of ownership of the outcome. This revision of assessment tools will make a powerful contribution to the consolidation of a needs-led approach.

3.54 A copy of the assessment of needs should normally be shared with the potential user, any representative of that user and all the people who have agreed to provide a service. Except where no intervention is deemed necessary, this record will normally be combined with a written care plan (the next stage of the care management process) setting out how the needs are to be addressed. Where other agencies are involved, they should also have a copy of these plans.

Assessing need
action checklist

Practitioners can use this list to check that key points are covered.

☐ 1 Has the scope of the assessment been negotiated with the potential user?

☐ 2 Has the appropriate setting been chosen?

☐ 3 Have expectations been clarified about the resources both practitioner and user bring to the assessment?

☐ 4 Have the potential users and carers been enabled to participate, with due sensitivity to their ethnic, cultural or communication needs?

☐ 5 Have users and carers had appropriate access to advocacy support?

☐ 6 Have the differing perceptions of need been reconciled or, if not, any differences recorded?

☐ 7 Have decisions on eligibility for assistance been explained to the user?

☐ 8 Have the eligible needs been prioritised?

☐ 9 Have objectives and criteria for measuring them been set for each of the prioritised needs?

☐ 10 Has a record of the assessment been shared with the user?

Stage 3

Comprehensive assessment guideline

Biographical details

These will include:

- Date of birth/age
- Address, telephone number
- Marital status
- Ethnic origin
- Religion
- Physical/learning disability or sensory impairment
- Household composition
- Employment (past and present)
- Name and address of next of kin/other responsible person
- GP – name, address, telephone number, NHS number (if available)

Self-perceived needs

The assessment should start from the applicant's own perception of their needs. This will determine the scope of the assessment and the degree of detailed enquiry of the relevant sections of any proforma.

Self-care

This encompasses basic activities such as eating, dressing, bathing and mobility and tasks such as shopping, dealing with money, cooking and using the telephone. These activities can be covered by a simple checklist or schedule, making use of knowledge held by agencies already involved.

The assessment must consider the person's maximum ability to perform such activities and his or her actual performance. For example, where there are problems of insight or depression, actual self-care can fall well below what that individual can potentially achieve. The practitioner must come to some judgement about the existing and probable motivation and the individual's capacity to achieve, maintain, or restore self-care.

Physical health

The request for social care may arise from problems of physical health so judgement is often necessary about whether a person requires an assessment from a health professional. There are many cases where a request for social care results from an otherwise unrecognised deterioration in physical health. The appropriate involvement of health staff through consultation with the GP will ensure that opportunities to improve health are not missed. Such involvement will also lead naturally to the provision of health inputs as part of the overall care plan.

Mental health

Here again a request for social care may mask a change in mental health which may, therefore, go untreated. Defects in such skills as memory can very easily be overlooked, especially as they are often accompanied by loss of insight. Such problems are more likely to be seen by the family than by the potential user. As with physical health, the assessing practitioner who has reason to believe there are mental health needs, should know when and how to involve the GP, community psychiatric nurse, approved social worker/mental health officer or psychiatric consultant (via GP).

Use of medicines

Many people must take medicines on a regular basis, especially those who have mental health problems or who have chronic conditions such as epilepsy or diabetes. Self-administration of medicines is not always possible and appropriate support may be needed. Problems associated with medicine usage may affect considerably the quality of life of individuals or their carers. The assessing practitioner needs to know when and how to involve the pharmacist, GP or nurse, as appropriate.

Abilities, attitudes and lifestyle

The needs of individuals can only be understood in the context of their lives as a whole. Each individual is unique in terms of their attitudes, abilities and approach to life. The assessment of need has to capture that uniqueness. This involves identifying the resources of individuals themselves and their care networks, before considering what additional resources may be required. The assessment has to focus on what is important to the individual to target any intervention in a way that will have the maximum beneficial effect on their quality of life.

Race and culture

It is important that all assessment staff have a knowledge and under-standing of racial and cultural diversity, and the impact of racism, as well as having access to specialist advice.

Personal history

Information relevant to personal resources and coping styles may come just as much from the past as from the present, for example, knowledge of a recent bereavement may have direct relevance to an understanding of current needs. However, the assessing practitioner should be guided by what is volunteered rather than seeking to compile a comprehensive personal history. Such depth is only relevant to intensive therapeutic intervention.

Needs of carers

This is still widely acknowledged to be a neglected area of practice. The user's perception of his or her needs is likely to be heavily influenced by the capacity and willingness of carers to continue or even increase the level of support that they are currently providing. It should never be assumed that the potential user and their carers share the same perceptions of need. In weighing the perceptions of carers, the practitioner must take account of all vested interests and give due weight to each perception.

Where an individual is dependent upon others to meet their care needs, the support required by those carers should be an integral part of the assessment, taking account of the following:

- their status or relationship with the individual
- the care they provide
- their expressed needs for support
- their wishes and preferences
- the nature of the relationship and attitude towards the individual
- the state of their mental and physical health
- their other commitments (family, job) – the impact of caring on those other commitments, their future prospects and the financial consequences
- the emotional or physical stress they are experiencing
- their likely future capacity and willingness to care.

The prime focus of an assessment must continue to be the needs of the user. If these are satisfactorily met the needs of carers may be too. Where this is not the case, carers should be offered a separate assessment of their own needs. Throughout the assessment process, carers should be fully aware of their entitlement within the constraints of confidentiality, to be involved and to be consulted.

Social network and support

Needs have to be understood in their social context, which extends beyond the contribution of direct carers to a wider set of social relationships. The extent to which an assessment engages with the individual's care network will vary with the complexity of the needs being addressed.

Care services

Many assessments will be undertaken in respect of individuals who are already receiving services. Their experience of those services may influence their presentation of any new needs and their expectation of future intervention. The assessment should, therefore, also consider the appropriateness of the services received for their current needs, opening up the possibility of a revised care plan.

Housing

Housing is important not only in terms of its cost, adequacy and suitability for a particular disability or set of disabilities but also in terms of its location, which may affect access to informal support and facilities. Assessors should always involve housing authorities and/or other relevant providers (for example, Housing Associations) if assessment indicates that there may be a housing need ❶. The aim should be to respect the preference of the user, wherever possible, accepting that the user's choice may involve some element of risk, for example, staying in accommodation deemed unsuitable by others.

Finance

Great tact is required in investigating financial means. However, it will be important to ensure that potential users are in receipt of their full social security entitlements, especially where receipt of certain benefits confers entitlements to other allowances or services, for example Attendance Allowance. This may have a material bearing on any request for additional assistance. Advice on handling money, or information about sources of such advice, should also be seen as a standard part of any assessment, including the involvement of the Court of Protection as appropriate. This consideration of finance will feed in to an assessment of financial means to determine the level of contribution for any services.

The assessment should also establish whether carers are receiving their full entitlements for the care that they provide. However, assessors should not assume that the financial resources of carers will be available to fund a user's care except where marital partners share an income. Any means testing should, therefore, be confined to the income of the user.

Transport

It is easy to overlook the importance of transport in community care, but it is fundamental in enabling services to get to people or people to services. Failure to recognise its contribution can lead to false perceptions of need, for example, providing meals on wheels to someone who fails to cook because they have no means of reaching the shops.

Risk

An evaluation of risk is central to any assessment whether that risk is occasioned by:

- environmental hazards, for example, gas fires for confused elderly people
- health, for example, diabetes, epilepsy
- behaviour, for example, psychotic episodes.

Where loss of insight is involved, the risks may be more apparent to others than to the potential user. However, subject to the user's capacity to take informed decisions, the assessing practitioner, in respecting the user's entitlement to self-determination and independence, must be guided by his or her own evaluation of risk. As such, the assessing practitioner may have to support the user against the possible over-protectiveness of others. At the same time, the practitioner has to weigh risks to the individual against those faced by carers or the wider community in arriving at a balanced judgement. That decision should be founded on the application of explicit policy criteria and be specifically recorded as part of the assessment.

Agencies and professions tend to vary in their perceptions of risk and crisis. Some will place the security of users above all other considerations, whereas others will emphasise the entitlement of the individual to take informed risks. Such differences should be clarified in agency agreements.

❶ In England Section 47(3) the *NHS and Community Care Act 1990* and in Scotland Section 12A of the Social Work (Scotland) Act 1968 as inserted by Section 55 of the *NHS and Community Care Act 1990.*

Stage 3

Stage 4
Care planning

To identify the most appropriate ways of achieving the objectives identified by the assessment of need and incorporate them into an individual care plan

¶ Process

4.1 Wherever possible, the practitioner responsible for assessing needs should carry on to relate those needs to the available resources. This will help to ensure that assessment does not become a theoretical exercise but is firmly rooted in practical reality.

4.2 As with the assessment of need, it is helpful if practitioners approach care planning as a series of linked activities:
- determine the type of plan
- set priorities
- complete definition of service requirements
- explore the resources of users and carers
- review existing services
- consider alternatives
- discuss options
- establish preferences
- cost care plan
- assess financial means
- reconcile preferences and resources
- agree service objectives
- co-ordinate plan
- fix review
- identify unmet need
- record the care plan.

▶ Determine the type of plan

4.3 Care plans will vary according to the complexity of need. If it is a simple need which can be met by a single service, the care planning can be very swiftly accomplished. **All users in receipt of a continuing service should have a care plan**, even if only a very brief one, which defines the user's needs and the objectives to be met by any service provided.

4.4 At the other extreme, care plans may be very complex, involving the co-ordination of services from a number of different agencies. The earlier that practitioners responsible for care planning are able to identify the contributing agencies and individuals the better they will be able to effect this co-ordination.

Stage 4

Stage 4

▶ Set priorities

4.5   The assessment should have prioritised the user's needs so they should be tackled in that priority order. Although, ideally, all needs should be assessed before progressing to the care planning stage, in practice, because of urgent needs, some services will have to be planned and arranged while other needs are still being assessed.

4.6   Care planning also has to be sufficiently flexible to adjust priorities as the needs of the user change.

▶ Complete definition of service requirements

4.7   The needs should have been defined at the assessment stage but more detail may be required to specify the service requirements. The aim of the care planning stage is to target any intervention as precisely as possible on the identified needs. To do this and work out how any intervention may cause as little disruption as possible, the practitioner will require an understanding of the individual's daily pattern of living.

4.8   Throughout, the practitioner will want to identify the factors that might help or hinder the achievement of the objectives defined at the assessment stage, such as the user's level of motivation or the flexibility of the service provider. These will help to frame the tactics that the practitioner adopts in negotiating the final plan with the user, carers or service providers. The example at the end of this guidance illustrates how these factors can be incorporated into an action plan. The service requirements will also include reference to the level of risk agreed with the users and carers at the assessment stage, in compliance with any agency guidelines on risk-taking.

▶ Explore the resources of users and carers

4.9   For the majority of users, **the aim will be to promote their independence**. For this reason, practitioners should begin by focusing on the resources of the user and how any strengths and abilities can be brought to bear to compensate for any difficulties, for example, tapping any determination to learn new skills. Similarly, ways and means of making better use of carers' resources should be examined at this stage, for example, asking them to visit at another time of day to meet a care need. However, the practitioner must not exploit the goodwill of carers or make unrealistic demands of users. Formal intervention should be kept to the minimum necessary in the interests of all concerned. From the agency's perspective, and often that of users and carers as well, care planning which enables users and carers to manage on their own is the most effective intervention of all.

▶ Review existing services

4.10   A majority of users will already be in receipt of some services and existing service providers will have been consulted in the course of the assessment. It may be that these services could be adjusted beneficially in the light of the objectives agreed during the assessment stage. If additional or new services are to be introduced, they will have to be interwoven with the existing services.

▶ Consider alternatives

4.11   However, in taking a fresh look at users' needs practitioners should not be constrained by the existing set of services. They should be equipped with the knowledge, or access to the knowledge, about the full range of services, not only in the statutory sector but also the independent sector. Even so, they may still have to undertake individual investigations in relation to specific needs, for example, identifying a community resource in a particular locality.

4.12   **Care planning should not be seen as matching needs with services 'off the shelf' but as an opportunity to rethink service provision for a particular individual.** Within resource constraints, practitioners should give full rein to their creativity in devising new ways of meeting needs, picking up clues from users and carers about what might be most relevant and effective. Clearly, those who have some or all of the budget delegated to them, will have greater scope to create alternatives or to press service providers into arranging different forms of service.

▶ Discuss options

4.13   Once identified, these **options should be fully discussed with the user and any relevant carers.** This may involve service providers being invited to discuss the detail of their services directly with users, or users being taken on observation visits. For those users who have limited knowledge of what services provide or have difficulty with the concept of choice, for example, those with learning disabilities, this exploration of options has to be as practical as possible so that they can begin to understand what it will mean for them personally.

▶ Establish preferences

4.14   Wherever possible, **users should be offered a genuine choice of service options,** appropriate to their ethnic and cultural background. This enables them to feel that they have some control over what is happening to them and reinforces their sense of independence. The degree of choice available will be affected by the level of devolved responsibility held by the care planner.

4.15   Some users, or those referring them, may have had very clear preferences about the service response from the outset. As a consequence, they may resist consideration of alternative options. However, the practitioners must satisfy themselves that the selected option is the one most suited to the identified needs. In exploring any alternatives, practitioners will have to demonstrate that they have given full consideration to the wishes of users and carers themselves. Where a practitioner is unable to accede to their preferences, users should receive a full explanation and be reminded of the complaints procedure.

▶ Cost care plan

4.16   Where practitioners have any delegated budgetary authority, it will be vital to have an accurate costing of the care plans. However, even where this is not the case, it is likely that practitioners will have to concern themselves with at least indicative costings as agencies strive to improve their cost-effectiveness. This will be particularly important as budgets are increasingly allocated to meeting needs (rather than to services) with prescribed ceilings of expenditure for specified levels of dependency or disadvantage. Users should always know the estimated cost to themselves of any options under active consideration.

4.17   Costing will obviously depend upon the availability of service costs. It is recognised that progress on this front may be variable as between health and social services/work authorities and between the private and voluntary sectors.

▶ Assess financial means

4.18   If charges are to be levied in respect of any services, then care planning will involve an assessment of the user's financial means and ability to pay. As a point of good practice, **no user should agree a care plan before they have been advised in writing of any charges involved.**

4.19   Local authorities cannot charge for care management and assessment but, within their discretion, are encouraged to levy charges on other services, subject to the user's ability to pay.

4.20   The rules governing financial assessment will be amended prior to the transfer of Social Security funding in April 1993. Further guidance on these matters will be issued in the course of 1992.

4.21   In the interim, local authorities may wish to review their charging policies to ensure that there are no financial incentives that run counter to the policy aim of maintaining people in the community. Under the post-1993 arrangements, it will be necessary for local authorities to enable users to use their own money or money from other sources to supplement any financial entitlement from the local authority, By doing this, users will increase their choice of service options in the independent sector.

4.22 The extent to which users are able to purchase statutory services over and above that determined by the assessment process will be defined as a matter of local policy. Any such income generation should be used to enhance, and not undermine, the capacity of the local authority **to respond in an equitable way to need**, irrespective of the user's financial means. Those with financial resources should not be allowed to take precedence over others with equal needs.

▶ Reconcile preferences and resources

4.23 Having established the wishes of the user and the cost of the selected options, these have to be reconciled with the available resources. This may be done by the practitioners alone, if they hold delegated budgets, or in conjunction with the relevant managerial and contracting staff.

4.24 In order to ensure consistency of resource allocation between users with similar needs, authorities or agencies may wish to issue guidelines to their staff on the levels of expenditure appropriate to different needs. Some discretion will be necessary if flexible, individualised responses are to develop.

4.25 It is at this stage that the practitioners have to balance their accountability to users and to their employing authority. This is more difficult where the practitioners have full financial responsibility and are responsible both for defining the needs and allocating the resources. In such circumstances, users may wish to avail themselves of independent representatives to promote their interests.

4.26 In order to decide on such matters, users should be informed where the responsibility for a resource allocation lies and the means of making representations under the complaints procedure, if dissatisfied. For their part, practitioners will require the support of their managers in discharging their responsibilities. They will inevitably experience the stress of identifying needs for which no resources are available.

▶ Agree service objectives

4.27 Having confirmed the service options that can be resourced, the next stage is to finalise the agreements with all the agencies and individuals who are to contribute to care plans. This will include the contribution of the user and carers themselves. The objectives of their inputs should be made clear to all contributors. These should be consistent with the objectives agreed with the user during the initial assessment stage. There should also be a common understanding of **how the achievement of these objectives will be measured**. For example, the rehabilitation of a depressed person may be gauged by the resumption of former interests or the establishment of new ones.

▶ Co-ordinate plan

4.28   Having negotiated a range of inputs, practitioners must integrate the parts into a coherent whole that makes sense to the user and their carers. All contributors to a care plan should be aware of the overall objectives as well as their own specific objectives so that they can be mutually supportive of one another. In complex situations, this may require a meeting of all parties but this should not be necessary in the majority of circumstances.

4.29   The care plan should also be sufficiently flexible to cater for contingencies and deal with difficulties and emergencies through contributors providing cover for one another. For example, a day centre might provide a meal if a relative is ill.

▶ Fix review

4.30   The user should be told the name the practitioner responsible for the implementation, monitoring and review of the care plan. This applies particularly where this responsibility is shared between a number of workers. In addition, **a date should be set for the first review** of the care plans. This is a simultaneous review of all the inputs so that their combined impact on the user's needs can be reassessed.

4.31   The interval between the formulation of the care plan and the first review will vary according to the changeability and complexity of needs. All parties should also be aware of the factors which will warrant the triggering of an earlier review.

▶ Identify unmet need

4.32   Having completed the care plan, the practitioner should identify any assessed need which it has not been possible to address and for what reason. This information should be fed back for service planning and quality assurance. It needs to be recorded and collated in a systematic way.

4.33   There may be benefit in differentiating between types of unmet need. These will include those that are:

- statutory obligations, for example, those included in the *Disabled Persons' (SCR) Act.*

- defined as entitlements under local policies, for example, failure to provide services within defined timescales.

- new needs, identified by assessing staff but falling outside current policies or criteria, for example, the emerging needs of those with HIV/AIDS.

4.34   There should also be a **ready means of prioritising these unmet needs.**

4.35 Needs may remain unmet for a number of reasons:
- resources are unable to meet demand.
- the quality and type of service is irrelevant to need, or unacceptable to users
- the conditions of service are inappropriate to need, for example, no weekend cover.

4.36 There will continue to be situations in which there is a mismatch between the solutions provided by the existing services and the solutions identified by users, carers and practitioners. Care planning has a contribution to make in minimising this mismatch by defining the disparity and promoting the appropriate changes in service.

▶ Record the care plan

4.37 Care plans should be set out in concise written form, linked with the assessment of need. The document should be accessible to the user, for example, in braille or translated into the user's own language. A copy should be given to the user but it should also, subject to constraints of confidentiality, be shared with other contributors to the plan. The compilation and distribution of such records has implications for the necessary levels of administrative support.

A care plan should contain the following:

- the overall objectives

- the specific objectives of:

  – users

  – carers

  – service providers

- the criteria for measuring the achievement of these objectives

- the services to be provided by which personnel/agency

- the cost to the user and the contributing agencies

- the other options considered

- any point of difference between the user, carer, care planning practitioner or other agency

- any unmet needs with reasons – to be separately notified to the service planning system

- the named person(s) responsible for implementing, monitoring and reviewing the care plan

- the date of the first planned review.

Stage 4

4.38   The care plan does not have a legal standing as a contract but, to reinforce the sense of commitment, contributors (including the user) may be asked to signify their agreement by signing. With or without signatures, the expectation is that contributors will honour their commitments and the care plan will be the means of holding them to account. As such, a care plan may be used as evidence in the consideration of a complaint.

4.39   **A care plan should be a blueprint for action.** It may, therefore, be framed as an action plan. An example of such a format is set out in the example of care management given in Annexe A at the end of this guidance.

Care planning action checklist

Practitioners can use this list to check that key points are covered.

☐ 1 Is the care plan based on the needs, priorities and objectives identified at the assessment stage?

☐ 2 Does it have a clear overall objective with specific objectives for all contributors, including the means of measuring their performance?

☐ 3 Does it set out the services to be supplied?

☐ 4 Does it make maximum use of the user's and carers' own resources?

☐ 5 Was the user offered a genuine choice of options?

☐ 6 Does it make co-ordinated and cost-effective use of the resources available to the user and agencies across the statutory and independent sectors?

☐ 7 Has it been costed?

☐ 8 Does it identify any unmet need?

☐ 9 Does it record any points of difference?

☐ 10 Have the practitioner(s) responsible for implementation, monitoring and review been decided?

☐ 11 Has a date for the first review been set?

☐ 12 Has a copy been given to the user and other contributors?

Stage 4

Stage 5
Implementing the care plan

To secure the necessary resources or services

5.1 The guiding principle of implementation should be **to achieve the stated objectives of the care plan with the minimum intervention necessary**. It should, therefore, seek to minimise the number of service providers involved. In several care management projects, this has been achieved by introducing generic care workers who perform a range of tasks that have traditionally been divided between home care and auxiliary nursing staff.

¶ Process

5.2 Wherever possible, the person responsible for devising the care plan should carry the responsibility for its implementation. That practitioner will have the benefit of a previously established relationship with the user and a shared commitment to make the care plan a reality. Where implementation is undertaken by a different practitioner, there must be feedback on the outcome to the author of the original care plan.

5.3 Whatever the complexity of the plan, there should always be one person responsible for its implementation. He/she will most often be employed by one of the statutory agencies but practitioners from external, independent agencies should not be excluded from assuming the role. The practitioner is accountable to both the user and the agency. The nature of the accountability will vary according to the level of delegated authority to purchase services. Where implementation is straightforward, responsibility for progress-chasing may be vested in vocationally qualified staff. However, where services have to be negotiated between agencies or new individualised services developed, this would normally be undertaken by personnel with professional training. Users should know the level of authority carried by the practitioner responsible for the implementation of their care plan.

5.4 Where a number of service inputs have to be co-ordinated, the practitioner's brokerage role can be compromised by having responsibility for **delivering** or **managing** any of those services. However, where only one service is involved, it may be more economic to delegate the responsibility for implementation to that service provider, so long as some external review of the service is retained.

Stage 5

5.5 Where efforts have not been made to distinguish the implementing and the service providing role, it is the experience of care management schemes that the implementation process is skewed in favour of the practitioner's particular expertise, for example, therapy as opposed to practical support services. In translating the care plan into reality, the implementation process should aim to be as faithful as possible to the original plan.

5.6 The tasks of implementation, already well known to many practitioners, may be listed as follows:
- determine the user/carer participation
- agree pace of implementation
- confirm budget
- check service availability
- renegotiate existing services
- contract with new services
- test options
- revise care plan and costing
- establish monitoring arrangements.

▶ Determine the user/carer participation

5.7 **The starting point for implementation should be the users and their carers** because all other inputs should be geared to supporting their contribution.

5.8 They should be encouraged to play **as active a part in the implementation of their care plan as their abilities and motivation allow.** It cannot be overstressed that the individual's sense of responsibility for their own life should not be diminished by the way that assistance is given. Users may require considerable reassurance and persuasion to accept help as may carers who feel threatened by such intrusion.

5.9 The successful care plan is one which interweaves formal interventions in a way that enhances, rather than undermines, existing care arrangements. This may require a significant adjustment on the part of the users and carers.

5.10 Direct cash payments to users cannot, in law, be made in England ❶ although they can be made in exceptional emergency situations in Scotland❷. The limitations do not, however, prevent authorities in England and Scotland from making alternative arrangements, such as voucher schemes. Indeed, some experimental projects are already in operation, for example, in Grampian Region. Many aspects of implementation may be delegated to users and carers, for example, renegotiating the contribution of carers or assisting in the recruitment of paid carers. Although only a minority of users may be able to play a major role in this way, it may be very important to their sense of independence that they are given that opportunity.

❶ Policy guidance para 3.17.

❷ Section 12 of the *Social Work (Scotland) Act 1968*.

Stage 5

5.11 All users should be included in the decision-making associated with the implementation of their care plans. If they are unable to participate, representatives should be enabled to speak on their behalf. This carries implications for resource allocation procedures. For example, allocation panels may promote the consistent distribution of resources but, unless safeguards are built in, they may also distance the user from the decision-making process.

▶ Agree pace of implementation

5.12 Work on implementation should commence as soon as the care plan has been finalised but **the pace at which it is implemented should be carefully negotiated with the user and their carers**. The acceptability of services may be greatly enhanced by the sensitivity with which they are introduced. Where a number of services are involved, the start may be staggered to allow the user and their carers a period of adjustment. However, some needs, such as medical conditions, may require an immediate response.

▶ Confirm budget

5.13 Whether or not practitioners have direct control of the budgets for purchasing services, they will want to confirm the availability of the relevant finance. This may involve negotiation with managers who control access to higher levels of funding. The respective levels of **budgetary authority** should be clearly understood by all practitioners.

▶ Check service availability

5.14 Implementation involves the practitioner in a constant round of checking on the availability of preferred services and confirming with the user whether they are prepared to wait for a particular service or to settle for another option. Where the latter applies, the **unavailability of preferred choices should be communicated to the service planning system**, because it will not be reflected in any waiting list.

▶ Renegotiate existing services

5.15 In a similar way, the existing pattern of services may have to be refashioned, either to accommodate changing needs or simply to achieve the desired objectives more effectively. These service providers may have to be challenged to deliver their services in a more flexible or imaginative way that is more appropriate to the individual needs of the user. The budget-holding practitioner obviously carries more influence in such negotiations than one who has to rely on persuasion alone.

◗ Contract with new services

5.16 In accessing new services, practitioners will have to adjust to the contracting arrangements that authorities and agencies are developing as part of the community care changes. Responsibility for contracting may be retained at a central level but it may be delegated, in whole or part, either to teams or to individual practitioners. In setting up complex packages of care, practitioners are likely to:

• require access to block contracts
• devise small-scale individual contracts.

5.17 Care management projects have demonstrated the value of practitioners being able to purchase gap-filling elements of service in order to customise a care package, for example, payments to neighbours to undertake specific care tasks.

5.18 To do this, practitioners will have to acquire skills in devising service specifications and quality standards and in negotiating and monitoring contracts. Their practice will have to be consistent with that of the contracting and inspection units of their authority. The common aim is **to produce a quality service as cost-effectively as possible within the agreed timescale**. To achieve such an aim, practitioners will have to be firm in setting standards, costs and deadlines and rigorous in holding service-providers to account.

◗ Test options

5.19 Although users may have tested out some options during the care planning stage, it is probable that this will continue through the implementation phase. Actual experience of preferred service options may prompt a desire to explore more alternatives. Some services may not be available, so others will have to be tried. Options offered will have to satisfy first of all the criteria of quality and cost set either by the authority or the practitioner to avoid disappointing the user at a later stage.

5.20 However careful the planning, implementation will involve some element of 'trial and error'. Given that some users will be loath to voice any reservations, practitioners will have to elicit users' feelings about a particular service option.

◗ Revise care plan and costing

5.21 The care plan should be revised in the light of the changes that have been made in the course of implementation. **The reason for any changes should be recorded**, for example, a lack of appropriate resource, changed preference or poor quality service. This revision should be done on the basis of agreement, or where this is not possible, any differences of view should be recorded. All contributors to a care plan should be notified of any significant revisions.

5.22   Where the implementation process has identified deficiencies, these should be notified to the relevant quarters, for example, service planning, inspection or quality assurance.

5.23   Any revisions of the care plan should be followed by a recalculation of the cost as the corrected baseline for future monitoring.

▶ Establish monitoring arrangements

5.24   The final task of the implementation phase consists in the establishment of **monitoring arrangements to ensure that the care plan remains on course.** The specific responsibility for monitoring will be allocated to someone who may, or may not, have carried out the previous tasks. All other contributors to the care plan will also have a share in the responsibility for monitoring. The implementing practitioner will alert the practitioner with monitoring responsibility about any adjustments in the ongoing implementation of the care plan.

Implementing the care plan action checklist

Practitioners can use this list to check that key points are covered.

☐ 1 Has the user been involved to the limit of their capacity in the implementation process?

☐ 2 Have the inputs of users and carers been maximised and have formal service inputs been geared to their support?

☐ 3 Has the pace of implementation been agreed with the user?

☐ 4 Has the budget for implementation been clearly defined, together with the responsibility for allocating that budget?

☐ 5 Have deficiencies in service availability and quality been notified to service planning and quality assurance/inspection respectively?

☐ 6 Have existing services been renegotiated to meet the care plan objectives more effectively?

☐ 7 Has the care plan been delivered to time and to quality?

☐ 8 Have resources been co-ordinated in a cost-effective way?

☐ 9 Have the reasons for any departure from the original care plan been recorded?

☐ 10 Have arrangements been established to monitor the ongoing implementation?

Stage 5

Stage 6
Monitoring

To support and control the delivery of the care plan on a continuing basis

6.1 The monitoring function has tended to be neglected in the past as a passive or reactive form of surveillance. Care management stresses the proactive role of monitoring in **supporting the achievement of set objectives over time and adapting the care plan to the changing needs of the user.**

6.2 The type and level of monitoring should relate to the **scale of intervention and the complexity of the needs** that are being addressed. Monitoring may be performed in a number of ways:

- home visits
- telephone calls
- letters
- questionnaires
- inter-staff/agency consultation
- observation.

6.3 All users who are in receipt of continuing services should have the benefit of some form of monitoring to ensure the appropriateness of that provision. However, the form of monitoring should be designed to cause as little disruption as possible to the users' daily pattern of living.

6.4 The purpose of monitoring should be fully explained to both users and carers. They should be given every encouragement to **play an active part** in the process. This might take the form of completing a progress chart, for example, on the building of an extension for a disabled person or a regular opportunity to share how they feel the care plan is progressing. Not only are they the people best qualified to comment on the services they are receiving, but they should be offered an opportunity to contribute to the corporate monitoring of services, through such mechanisms as user/carer consultative groups.

¶ Process

6.5 Wherever possible, the practitioner responsible for assessment, care planning and implementation should continue to hold the responsibility for monitoring. This provides continuity for the user and a level of commitment that is unlikely to be shared by a practitioner who has been less involved.

Stage 6

6.6   Although monitoring should be co-ordinated by one practitioner, the responsibility should be shared with others:

- user and carers – as recipients as well as contributors
- significant others (neighbours, volunteers) – as contributors
- service providers – as monitors of their own services
- first line manager – as overseer of quality assurance
- purchasing unit – as monitor of contracts
- inspection unit – as monitor of quality standards in residential care.

6.7   Although the practitioner is independent to the extent of not being directly involved in service provision, objectivity may be dimmed by dint of supporting contributors over time. It is for this reason that those external to the immediate care arrangements, for example, first line managers and purchasing units, should have a continuing role in challenging any complacency.

6.8   The monitoring practitioner has a central role in co-ordinating these different levels of monitoring and ensuring that consistent criteria or standards are being applied.

6.9   Monitoring embraces a number of different tasks:

- monitor the care plan objectives
- co-ordinate the inputs
- ensure that contributions are delivered according to specification
- oversee the quality of care
- manage the budget
- support users, carers and service providers
- fine tune the care plan
- contribute to the review process.

▶ Monitor the care plan objectives

6.10   The aim of monitoring is **to facilitate the achievement of the objectives set in the care plan.** The monitoring practitioner has to keep each contributor on track in terms of delivering their specific objectives. Progress should be measured on a regular basis against the criteria or indicators defined in the care plan.

▶ Co-ordinate the inputs

6.11   The more contributors there are, the more important the role of co-ordination. The practitioner is at the hub **ensuring that contributors' efforts are complementary** to one another and that all necessary information is shared. The practitioner has a key role in managing any changes in the pattern of services in a way that preserves continuity of care.

⬗ Ensure that contributions are delivered according to specification

6.12 The contribution of all participants, including that of the user and their carers should be specified in the original care plan. Failure to deliver by any one contributor may jeopardise the whole plan. The contribution may be from an unpaid carer or a paid service provider, so the practitioner will have to adopt a variety of approaches in maintaining the package of care. Where the practitioner has developed a one-off service for an individual, he/she has a heightened responsibility to monitor that provision.

⬗ Oversee the quality of care

6.13 The expected quality standards should be known and accepted by all parties but the practitioner is clearly in a stronger position to enforce such standards when they are specified in service providers' contracts than when they are a matter of informal understanding with unpaid carers or volunteers. Whereas each contributor has a responsibility for the quality for their own input, the monitoring practitioner is accountable for the **total quality of care** as it is experienced by the user.

6.14 Quality lies in the attention to detail that matters to the individual. Therefore, the practitioner has the role of sensitising contributors to the personal requirements of the user, for example, the way a disabled person prefers to be lifted. The pursuit of **improvement in quality should be a never-ending quest** for the monitoring practitioner.

⬗ Manage the budget

6.15 The monitoring practitioner may have direct responsibility for the budget or he/she may be required to maintain a surveillance on cost. This aspect of monitoring will assume increasing importance as financial responsibility is devolved and budgets are developed for individual users. Few practitioners have had to deal in this area in the past. However, care management schemes, for example, Thanet, have developed simple accounting systems that practitioners are able to operate, after only limited training in financial management.

⬗ Support users, carers and service providers

6.16 One of the most significant and time-consuming elements of monitoring is the support which it may be necessary to give to users and carers, in particular, but also to service providers.

6.17 Support may take different forms:
- counselling
- progress-chasing
- resolving conflicts or difficulties.

6.18   In order to be supportive, monitoring must strike a balance. Commitment to a care plan is sustained more by positive than negative feedback so, in reminding contributors of what remains to be achieved, the monitoring practitioner must underline what has already been accomplished.

▸ Fine tune the care plan

6.19   It is the task of the monitoring practitioner to be alert to any changes in the needs and preferences of users and their carers and to make any minor adjustments in the care plan that may be necessary. The monitoring practitioner only has limited scope because any major change would normally be sanctioned by a review.

6.20   However, even minor changes should not happen by default, but as a matter of deliberate planning. The reasons for **any** changes should be recorded and reconsidered at the next review. Monitoring should contribute to a **progressive refinement of the original care plan,** on the basis of experience.

▸ Contribute to the review process

6.21   It is important that monitoring is both **undertaken and recorded in a systematic way**. Monitoring provides the evidence on which the care plan is re-evaluated at each review. It should record the progress, or otherwise, in achieving the care plan objectives.

6.22   Systematic recording serves another purpose. It provides a basis of accountability between practitioners and managers as it enables the latter to exercise their monitoring function. This takes on added significance, given the increasing autonomy of practitioners under the new arrangements.

6.23   Monitoring should provide early warning of difficulties that might trigger a review before the next scheduled date. The criteria for triggering an early review should be known to all contributors. This applies particularly to the monitoring of acceptable levels of risk. Where a user's capabilities are diminishing, it is a task of monitoring to identify when the next threshold of vulnerability has been crossed that requires a formal review of the care plan.

Monitoring
action checklist

Practitioners can use this list to check that key points are covered.

☐ 1 Is the type and level of monitoring appropriate to the care plan?

☐ 2 Are users and carers actively involved?

☐ 3 Is the monitoring of the care plan co-ordinated with that of the contracting and inspection units?

☐ 4 Is the achievement of objectives regularly monitored against the criteria or indicators defined in the care plan?

☐ 5 Does the monitoring practitioner continue to co-ordinate the contributions to the care plan?

☐ 6 Are services or contributions regularly checked against the original specification?

☐ 7 Are the same quality standards consistently applied by all contributors?

☐ 8 Is the care plan being delivered within budget?

☐ 9 How regular is the support for users, carers and service providers?

☐ 10 Are the reasons for minor changes in the care plan recorded?

☐ 11 Is monitoring systematically recorded?

☐ 12 Are the criteria for triggering an early review known to all contributors?

Stage 6

Stage 7
Reviewing

To reassess, at specific intervals, needs and service outcomes with a view to revising the care plan

7.1 Like monitoring, reviewing has traditionally been afforded a low priority. Where reviews have taken place, they have often been subject to lengthy delays. Care management gives reviewing a higher profile. **It is the mechanism by which changing needs are identified and services adapted accordingly.**

7.2 Like assessment, **reviewing should be needs-based**. The prime focus of a review should not be the services provided but the needs, views and preferences of users and carers and the effectiveness of services in addressing those needs. Wherever possible, one review should consider altogether the services that are being received by a user. There should be a standard expectation that the needs of all users in receipt of a continuing service or services will be reviewed at periodic intervals. It is the only way of ensuring that any intervention remains effective.

¶ Process

7.3 The **scope** of a review will depend upon the complexity of need and the level of invested resources. The **frequency** will be governed by how much the needs are subject to change.

7.4 The **form and venue** of the review should be substantially governed by what is judged to be the most effective way of involving users and carers. It may, therefore, be appropriate for the core part of the review to be undertaken in the user's own home.

7.5 The review does not have to be undertaken through meetings of all participants. It may consist in a series of consultations either by telephone, letter or direct meetings, on separate occasions to suit the convenience of participants. However, it should be no less rigorous or systematic for being undertaken on a phased basis.

7.6 All those involved in the original care planning or last review should be consulted. All participants to the review should be given sufficient notice to prepare their contribution. This applies particularly to the users and carers themselves to whom the purpose and content of a review should be fully explained together with their entitlement to have a representative present, if they wish.

7.7 Large scale review meetings should only rarely be necessary. These are often intimidating to users and carers, difficult to organise and demanding of scarce professional time. However, if they are called, as with case conferences, their purpose should be clearly defined and they should be well chaired and structured so that they do not inhibit the contribution of users and carers.

7.8   Such review meetings may be thought appropriate where:

- needs have changed for reasons not understood by any of the agencies

- new and complex care arrangements have to be established at speed, for example, in response to a crisis

- there is continuing conflict or lack of co-ordination between contributing individuals and/or agencies.

7.9   Where practitioners find themselves in any measure of conflict with other participants, it may be more appropriate for the review to be chaired by a first line manager. However, where complaints have been raised, these may be dealt with more appropriately under the complaints procedures. All parties should be aware of their entitlements under the respective procedures.

7.10 In terms of accumulating an understanding of a user's needs over time, there are considerable advantages in the same practitioner carrying through responsibility from assessment to review. Where this is not possible, there should be a feedback loop to those responsible for the other phases of care management.

7.11 If the focus on needs is to be preserved, the reviewing practitioner should not normally be directly involved in either delivering or managing the services received. Where this is not feasible for all users, such a separation of role should at least be maintained in the reviewing of provision to users with complex needs. Where only one service is being received and that service provider undertakes the reviewing function, there should be some safeguard of objectivity perhaps by means of a management check.

7.12 As with assessment, there may be organisational benefits from adopting a standard format in that it aids the consistent collection of data for the purposes of service planning and quality assurance.

7.13 A review fulfils a number of different purposes which are to:

- review the achievement of care plan objectives

- examine the reasons for success or failure

- evaluate the quality and cost of the care provided

- reassess current needs

- reappraise eligibility for assistance

- revise the care plan objectives

- redefine the service requirements

- recalculate the cost

Stage 7

- notify quality assurance/service planning of any service deficiencies or unmet needs
- set the date for the next review
- record the findings of the review.

▶ Review the achievement of care plan objectives

7.14 The starting point for any review should be the perception of the user and their carers of what progress has been made in achieving the stated objectives. This can then be compared with the views of service providers, both as regards the overall objective and the specific objectives set for each service. On the basis of these contributions, the reviewing practitioner should come to a balanced judgement about the **realism of the original objectives and their continuing relevance**.

▶ Examine the reasons for success or failure

7.15 Lessons should be learned from both achievements and set-backs. Analysis of the reasons for past success and failure should inform future action.

▶ Evaluate the quality and cost of the care provided

7.16 Reviewing provides an opportunity for formal stock-taking. By drawing on evidence from the monitoring process, the review can establish whether services have maintained the specified quality of care within the budget limits. Again, it will be important to explore the reasons for any failure. A judgement on **the cost-effectiveness of current services should underpin the planning of future service provision.**

▶ Reassess current needs

7.17 The review will not repeat the original assessment but it should not so concentrate on past needs that it remains blind to new or changed needs that warrant some form of assessment. The assumption should be that needs and the user's preferences in relation to those needs are in a constant state of change and that services should change as a consequence.

▶ Reappraise eligibility for assistance

7.18 If the aim of a care plan is to promote independence, success may be measured by the capacity of the individual to cope without services. Needs are subject to change but so are the policies of the authority or agency. The increasing emphasis on targeting will mean that reviews not only confirm or increase services, they will also sanction their reduction and withdrawal. Where the level of assistance is adjusted, the reasons for that change should be **explained to the user** or their representative.

Stage 7

◗ Revise the care plan objectives

7.19   The original objectives should be re-evaluated in the light of past progress towards their achievement. In addition, attention should be given to the specific short-term objectives of each service provider, setting targets that build on past achievement and specifying how they will be measured. These objectives should be revised with the agreement of the user, taking full account of his/her wishes and preferences.

◗ Redefine the service requirements

7.20   The recasting of the care plan may require the renegotiation of service contracts or at least some redefinition of the type and volume of services to be provided and the way they are to be delivered.

◗ Recalculate the cost

7.21   The review has to reaffirm or revise the budget for the period up to the next review. This may be subject to ratification at a higher managerial level. At the same time, any revision of the charges to the user should be specified, taking account of any changes in the user's financial circumstances.

◗ Notify quality assurance/service planning of any service deficiencies or unmet needs

7.22   In the same way that any deficiencies in the type, quality or availability of services are notified to quality assurance and service planning systems at the care planning stage, so this should be repeated at each review, if any new shortcomings are identified. In particular, it should be noted where these deficiencies result in any unmet needs.

◗ Set the date of the next review

7.23   Agencies may wish to set guidelines for the minimum frequency of reviews, for example, not less than once a year. However, the interval of reviews should be related to the pace of change in the user's needs as this determines the need to revise the care plans. Whatever the frequency, there should always be the contingency of an earlier review, if circumstances dictate. However, **each review should set the date for the next** because that sets the deadline for achieving the next set of objectives. Such a discipline will also counter the danger of reviews being delayed. The practitioner who holds the monitoring responsibility for the next review period should be identified at the same time.

◗   Record the findings of the review

7.24 A copy of the review report should be given to the user and,
      subject to the constraints of confidentiality, it should also be
      shared with all other contributors to the review.

A standard schedule for the recording of reviews
would include:

- an evaluation of the achievement of objectives with reasons for
  success or failure

- an evaluation of the quality and cost of the services provided

- a reassessment of current needs

- a reappraisal of eligibility for assistance with reasons for any
  changes

- a revision of the care plan objectives

- any required changes in service provision

- a revised costing of the care plan

- any points of difference between parties to the reviews

- identification of any unmet need and any continuing or new service
  deficiencies

- the date of the next planned review and confirmation of the
  practitioner with monitoring responsibility for the next review
  period.

Reviewing action checklist

Practitioners can use this list to check that key points are covered.

☐   1   Is the review taking place on the scheduled date?

☐   2   Has the type of review been geared to the needs under consideration?

☐   3   Is the review centred on the needs and preferences of the user rather than on the services provided?

☐   4   Are all the service providers involved in the review?

☐   5   Is the reviewing practitioner independent of the service provision?

☐   6   How have the user and carer been enabled to participate and have their wishes been taken fully into account?

☐   7   Has the review addressed both the positive and negative aspects of the care plan?

☐   8   Has the evaluation of services weighed both quality and cost?

☐   9   Have the reasons for any change in assessed eligibility been explained to the user?

☐   10   Has the review been recorded, as indicated?

Stage 7

Annexe A
Example of care management

Mrs Alice Baker is to be discharged from hospital following a stroke. The way her needs are addressed illustrate the seven stages of care management.

▶ ## Stage 1
Publishing information

The ward sister ensures that she receives the information booklet on rehabilitation services for stroke victims and the leaflet on the volunteer 'Stroke Support Scheme', following discussion with her about her likely difficulties upon returning home.

▶ ## Stage 2
Determining level of assessment

The ward sister completes a referral form to the hospital social work team, detailing Mrs Baker's concerns about managing at home, both immediately and in the longer term.

On the basis of that information, the social services team leader decides that Mrs Baker should receive a comprehensive assessment, co-ordinated by a social worker. This staff member attends the ward round; she has an initial interview with Mrs Baker and arranges for assessments to be completed by a physiotherapist and occupational therapist.

▶ ## Stage 3
Assessing need

The social worker identifies that, although Mrs Baker is anxious to retain her independence, her confidence has been severely affected and she is unsure what level of support her daughter, who lives nearby, will be able to give her, because she has a large family of her own.

The physiotherapist confirms that Mrs Baker has suffered a significant loss of functioning in her right arm and leg; the prognosis is encouraging but uncertain and depends upon the patient's sustained commitment to rehabilitation.

The occupational therapist takes Mrs Baker on a visit back to her council home before advising her that she will initially have difficulty with most aspects of self-care . She will not be able to climb stairs, so sleeping and toileting facilities will have to be provided downstairs.

Despite her misgivings, Mrs Baker wishes to:

- return home as soon as support services can be arranged
- re-establish as much independence as possible
- review future options in six months in the light of progress.

Her daughter is supportive of this intention but limited in the amount of support she is able to give.

▶ Stage 4
Care planning

The social worker clarifies the likely discharge date with the consultant; she refers Mrs Baker to the intensive discharge service and 'Meals on Wheels'. A care plan is devised in which:

- the discharge service covers getting up and going to bed for a maximum of six weeks
- 'Meals on Wheels' are available five days a week and the daughter provides cover at weekends
- Mrs Baker agrees to meet the assessed charges
- the daughter undertakes to visit three times during the week at specified times, synchronised with contacts from the community nurse and social worker and the weekly outpatient physiotherapy
- the occupational therapist undertakes to complete her initial assessment within one week of discharge and arrange provision of the appropriate disability equipment.

All visitors agree to complete a diary sheet to be kept by Mrs Baker and to review the situation after six weeks. Mrs Baker and all contributors receive a copy of the written care plan which spells out the primary objective of rehabilitating Mrs Baker and restoring her confidence.

▶ Stage 5
Implementing the care plan

The ward sister confirms the date of discharge, so the social worker alerts all the relevant agencies and individuals. The daughter sets up the downstairs bedroom and takes delivery of the commode, ordered by the ward sister from the home loans service.

The social worker negotiates the budgetary allocation for the intensive discharge service and the 'Meals on Wheels' service. She also checks that all parties are able to honour their commitments.

▶ Stage 6
Monitoring

One week after discharge, the social worker takes stock with Mrs Baker over how well the arrangements are working and makes some minor amendments to the programme of visiting, following consultation with the individuals affected. Those who have failed to complete the diary sheet are reminded of the importance of the record. Mrs Baker decides that she would like to make contact with the 'Stroke Support Scheme', so this is arranged by the community nurse. The social worker confirms that the daughter is able to continue with the agreed level of support. As Mrs Baker improves, the level of support is gradually reduced.

▶ Stage 7
Reviewing

After six weeks, the social worker obtains feedback from all involved on the progress of the arrangements.

This is discussed with Mrs Baker at a meeting to which the daughter is invited, at Mrs Baker's request. Apart from a complaint about the unvaried menu of 'Meals on Wheels', there is general agreement that the arrangements have worked reasonably well and that Mrs Baker will be able to cope with the scaled-down input of the domiciliary care service after the intensive discharge service has withdrawn. However, because Mrs Baker is disappointed with the pace of her rehabilitation, she requests that the social worker instigates an assessment by the Housing Department to explore alternative housing options.

A revised care plan is drawn up and re-distributed following consultation with all the contributors, setting the next review for a further six weeks' time. Mrs Baker's complaint about 'Meals on Wheels' is fed back into the quality assurance system. The budgetary allocation for the revised plan is re-negotiated by the social worker.

Action plan

Mrs Alice Baker to be discharged from hospital following stroke

Identified needs/problems (in priority order)	Objectives	Helping factors	Hindering factors	Timescale	Resources needed	Costings	Action by whom	Action – taken	Date
Unable to reach toilet upstairs	Provision of equipment within 48 hours prior to hospital discharge	Co-operative consultant re: discharge date	Access to property	Immediate	Commode on loan		Order from loans service-ward sister		
Unsupported home situation	Daily support visits for six weeks	Positive motivation of user / Availability of intensive discharge service	Lack of support network / Lack of 7 day meals service	Six weeks (then review)	Intensive domiciliary care / 'Meals on Wheels'		Assessment: Domiciliary care organiser / Social worker to offer counselling support re: stroke		
	Specified increase in family support	Daughter lives nearby	Daughter's large family	Two weeks	Three visits per week		Social worker to negotiate		
Loss of functioning in right arm/leg	Restore full functioning	Encouraging prognosis	User's loss of confidence	Three months (then review)	Physiotherapy Disability equipment		Assessments: Physio and occupational therapist / Liaison with domiciliary care organiser / Support – all staff		
Possible long-term unsuitability of home	Clarify and discuss housing/care options within six months	Option of nearby sheltered housing	Uncertainty of rehabilitation outcome	Six months	Housing options: Adaptation / House transfer / Sheltered housing / Residential care / Care by relative		Explore options: Occupational therapist / Social worker / Consult with housing – social worker		

TOTAL =

Annexe B
DH/SSI and Scottish Office Publications and commissioned studies

▶ Care management and assessment

Beardshaw, V and Towell, D (March 1990) 'Assessment and Case Management' in *Briefing Paper No 10*, Kings Fund

Silvey, J and Stevenson, O (March 1991) *Co-operation in Community Care: report of a seminar on joint working between Health and Social Services*, School of Social Studies, Nottingham University

Neill, J (ed) (July 1991) *Getting the Message Across*, National Institute for Social Work, HMSO

(July 1991) *Assessment Systems and Community Care*, SSI/Social Information Systems Ltd, HMSO

Beardshaw, V (Forthcoming 1991) *Mutual Aid Information Network: A Network for Developing Informed Approaches to Assessment and Care Management*, King's Fund

(Forthcoming 1991) *Empowering Users*, National Institute for Social Work

▶ Training

(September 1990) *Training for Community Care: a strategy*, HMSO

(July 1991) *Care Kaleidoscope – Simulation Exercise*, HMSO

(Forthcoming 1991) *Joint Personal Social Services/NHS Community Care Training Strategy*, HMSO

▶ Mental illness

(September 1990) *Mental Illness Specific Grant – Monitoring Arrangements*, HMSO

(Forthcoming 1991) *Building a Mental Health Service*, HMSO

▶ Complaints

(August 1991) *Complaints Procedures: Practice Guidance*, HMSO

▶ Inspection units

(January 1991) *Inspection Units: Issues in Implementation*, HMSO

(January 1991) *Inspection Units: Training Issues*, HMSO

▶ Community care plans

Wistow, G (1990) *Community Care Planning: A Review of Past Experience and Future Imperatives*, Nuffield Institute

(January 1991) *Community Care Plans: The First Steps*, Department of Health

▶ Purchasing/contracting

Flynn, N and Common, R (April 1990) *Contracts for Community Care*, London Business School, HMSO

(February 1991) *Implementing Community Care: Managing the Information*, Price Waterhouse for ADSS/CIPFA, HMSO

(February 1991) *Implementing Community Care: Software Strategy*, Price Waterhouse for ADSS/CIPFA, HMSO

(February 1991) *Implementing Community Care: Information Strategy*, Price Waterhouse for ADSS/CIPFA, HMSO

(April 1991) *Practice Guide on Purchase of Service*, HMSO

(April 1991) *Implementing Community Care: Purchaser, Commissioner and Provider Roles*, Price Waterhouse, HMSO

▶ Caring for quality series

(1989) *Towards a Climate of Confidence, Overview Report of National Inspection of Residential Care for Elderly People,* HMSO

(1989) *Homes are for Living in – North West Region,* HMSO

(1990) *Home Care Overview Report,* HMSO

(1990) *Inspecting Home Care Services: A Guide to SSI Method,* HMSO

(1990) *Guidance on Standards for Residential Homes for Elderly People,* HMSO

(1990) *Guidance on Standards for Residential Homes for People with a Physical Disability,* HMSO

(1990) *Guidance on Standards for Residential Homes for People with Mental Disorders,* HMSO

(Forthcoming 1991) *Guidance on Standards for Residential Homes for People with a Learning Disability,* HMSO

▶ Scottish Office Publications

(October 1990) 'Guide to the NHS and Community Care Act' in *Social Work Services Group Circular SW6/1990,*

(October 1990) 'Inspection of Establishments: Organisation and Role of Inspection Units', in *Social Work Services Group Circular SW9/1990*

(October 1990) 'Mental Illness Specific Grant' in *Social Work Services Group Circular SW10/1990*

(January 1991) 'Community Care Planning' in *Social Work Services Group Circular SW1/1991*

(February 1991) 'Complaints Procedures' in *Social Work Services Group Circular SW5/1991*

(March 1991) 'Housing and Community Care' in *Scottish Office Environment Department Circular ENV8/1991*

(May 1991) *Practice Guidance – Inspection Units: Establishing Good Practice,* SWSG

(May 1991) *Community Care Planning: Development Projects,* SWSG Report (Further Report in Autumn 1991)

(June 1991) 'Assessment and Care Management' in *Social Work Services Group Circular SW11/1991*

(June 1991) *Discussion Paper: Improving Quality Assurance in Community Care,* SWSG

(July 1991) *Practice Guidance: A Right to Complain,* SWSG

(August 1991) *Getting to Know You: a report of a project on user and carer participation in assessment,* SWSG

Training

(October 1990) 'Community Care in Context: Unit 1' in *The Community Care Training Programme,* University of Dundee, Department of Social Work

(June 1991) *Introduction to Community Care: A Training Pack,* prepared by ADSW, CCETSW, COSLA (available from CCETSW)

(Forthcoming 1991) 'Planning and Managing Community Care: Unit 2' in *The Community Care Training Programme,* University of Dundee, Department of Social Work

Annexe C
Selected reading

British Association of Social Workers (1990) *Managing Care,* BASW
A thoughtful practitioners' perspective.

Centre for Policy on Ageing (1990) *Community Life: A Code of Practice for Community Care*, CPA
A readable exposition of principles of good practice.

Challis, D et al (1990) *Case Management in Social and Health Care,* PSSRU, University of Kent
An account of the Gateshead Community Care Scheme with helpful introduction on care management.

Neill, J (1989) *Assessing Elderly People for Residential Care: a practical guide*, National Institute for Social Work
A sensitive guide to assessment practice.

Practice and Development Exchange (1989) *Shared Care: Towards Developing Partnerships between Health and Social Services Staff and the People They Serve*, National Institute for Social Work
Advice on how to develop more equal relationships between practitioners and users derived from practice.

Richardson, A et al (1989) *A New Deal for Carers,* Kings Fund
Practical suggestions for improving the lot of carers.

Seed, P (1990) *Introducing Network Analysis in Social Work,* Jessica Kingsley Publishers
Examples from practice of working with informal care networks.

Biggs, S and Weinstein, J (1991) *Towards a Practice Curriculum for Community Care: Assessment, Care Management and Inspection*, Central Council for Education and Training for Social Workers
An initial analysis of the required skills.

Annexe D
Advisory group on care management and assessment

* Mr Simon Allard	Assistant Chief Inspector, SSI (Chair)
* Miss Carolyn Hey	Deputy Chief Inspector, SSI
* Miss Joan Baraclough	Assistant Chief Inspector, SSI
* Miss Janet Morgan	Assistant Secretary, DH
* Mr Cyril Stone	Assistant Secretary, DH
* Mr Michael Skinner	Principal Officer, DH
* Dr Pamela Mason	Senior Medical Officer, DH
* Dr Bill Miller	Senior Medical Officer, DH
* Dr Stewart Munday	Senior Medical Officer, DH
* Mrs Daphne Patey	Principal Nursing Officer, DH
* Mrs Rosemary Bowden	Occupational Therapy Officer, DH
* Mr Bob Welch	Lead Inspector, SSI
Ms Linda Hunt	Senior Social Work Advisor, Social Work Services Group, Scottish Office
Mrs Brenda Holmes	Social Work Advisor, Social Work Services Group, Scottish Office
Ms Rosemary Evans	Health and Social Work Department, Welsh Office
Mr Norman Chambers	Department of Health and Social Services, Northern Ireland Office
Mr David Tombs	Director of Social Services, Hereford and Worcester
Mr Norman Warner	Director of Social Services, Kent
Ms Gwen Swire	British Association of Social Workers
Mr Vic Citarella	Social Care Association
* Mr Laurie Ford	SSI (Administrative Secretary)

* also members of the Departmental Implementation Group on Care Management and Assessment

Other members of the Departmental Implementation Group:

Mrs Linda Hoare	SSI Inspector
Mr Peter Stone	SSI Inspector
Mr Roy Pearson	SSI Inspector
Mr Barry Norman	SSI Inspector
Mr David Tomlinson	SSI Inspector
Mr Colin Bott	SSI Inspector

Consultation group – Practice Guide

Mr Simon Allard	Assistant Chief Inspector, SSI (Chair)
* Mr Bob Welch	Lead Inspector, SSI
Dr Ann Richardson	Research Adviser
Dr Peter Horrocks	Director of Health Policy, Yorkshire RHA
Mr Nick Skinner	Community Nursing Adviser, Winchester DHA
Ms Carol Underwood	Principal Service Manager (Physical Disability) Croydon SSD
Dr Phillip Seed	Department of Social Work, Dundee University
Mr Les McEwan	Deputy Director, Lothian Social Work Department
Mr Ted Unsworth	Deputy Director, Cambridgeshire
Mr Trevor Brown	Assistant Director, Northampton SSD
Ms Judy Taylor	Principal Officer, Bexley SSD
Ms Sue Milne	Principal Officer, Kent SSD
Mr Tony Elson	Director, Kirklees SSD
Mr Chris Davies	Director, Somerset SSD
Mr David Gwyther	Principal Officer, Somerset SSD
Ms Gwen Swire	British Association of Social Workers
Mr Vic Citarella	Social Care Association
Mr Simon Whitehead	Associate Director, National Development Team

* Responsibility for drafting the text.

Consultants:

Dr David Challis	PSSRU, Kent University
Dr Sally Baldwin	SPRU, York University
Dr David Towell	King's Fund Centre
Prof Olive Stevenson	Nottingham University

Secretarial work:
Mrs June Green
Miss Barbara Padmore

Printed in the United Kingdom for HMSO.
Dd.296118, 2/93, C40, 3396/4, 5673, 232428.